ENDORSEMENTS

So, after reading your book I feel I have made a new friend. The book is not just raw, it is encouraging. You have given those struggling with mental illness hope. Thank you for exposing your struggles to help others.

—DEBBIE CARDINALE, *friend*

•

Cindy is a remarkable woman! She not only conquered her cancer, but she also maintained all of her responsibilities as a wife, mother, grandmother, friend and fulfilled all of her civic involvements during her cancer treatments. Not only that, but she also reached out to others battling cancer, encouraging them, and even drove a cancer patient to her ongoing treatment appointments, while she was undergoing treatment. Cindy is a true servant leader, a champion in my book! I am honored to have her as a friend, and also to serve alongside her, as a member of the San Luis Obispo County Juvenile Justice and Delinquent Prevention Commission.

—JAMES W. BRABECK, *Community Leader*

•

Cindy Wittstrom has been my patient since 2009. She was diagnosed and treated for breast cancer in 1999, thankfully with no recurrence. She experienced postpartum depression in 1979 and did not show any signs of bipolar disease until 1997. Cindy has gone beyond simply enduring bipolar disorder, she has truly lived her life as a wife, mother, grandmother, community volunteer and has played an active role in her church. She has not "become" her illness. She has never given up. May her story inspire others to do the same.

—MARGARET K. BAUMAN, MD

I met Cindy as she was navigating her world in a state of exhaustion and bewilderment. Her state is much different today. She is now empowered, as evidenced by her completion of this book. In order to obtain a healthy recovery and stability, education and communication must be utilized. Cindy and her family have done the necessary work.

—TIA GLICKMAN, PhD LMFT

Bernie, our leader, liked to say, "I collect strays…successful women who need friends." Hence, the formation of a group of seven Christian sisters. Our discussions of honesty and transparency deepened as Cindy revealed her "secret" of Bipolar Illness. This revelation enabled all of us to trust and share, sometimes very personal struggles. It is an honor to walk beside and support Cindy on her journey toward the light at the end of the tunnel.

—KAREN K. JACOBSMA, *Santa Margarita Community Church*

From the sociable 4-year-old visiting with customers at her mom's Big Orange in Bradley, to the outgoing 13-year-old *fashionista,* to the 17-year-old PRHS straight-A student and varsity cheerleader, Cindy's always been an achiever. To learn of her battle with mental illness was shocking. She kept her story close for decades. Until now.

—PAULA ELSEY, *Book Editor*

Finally, a book about mental illness for the "average Joe and Jill!" In *When the Brakes Fail*, Cindy walks you through the subtleties and gradations of daily life that can ignite an individual's issues with mental health. She uses her own story to paint a picture of what it's like to sleuth out a diagnosis and discover effective treatment options. Readers end up cheering with her, as her hard work, sense of humor, strength and faith bring her to a place of peace.

—MALEI WEIR, *Marketing Consultant*

WHEN THE BRAKES FAIL

NOTABLE QUOTATIONS

There is a crack in everything.
That's how the light gets in.
        — LEONARD COHEN

Hope is being able to see that
there is light despite all of the
darkness.
        —DESMOND TUTU

Some people won't love you no
matter what you do, and some
people won't stop loving you no
matter what you do. Go where
the love is.
        —UNKNOWN

Come to me, all who labor and are
heavy laden, and I will give
you rest.
        —MATTHEW 11:2

The forces that are for you
are greater than the forces
against you.
        —JOEL OSTEEN

We need never be hopeless
because we can never be
irreparably broken.
        —ALBERT EINSTEIN

Nothing can dim the light
which shines from within.
        —MAYA ANGELOU

Be joyful in hope, patient in
affliction, faithful in prayer.
        —ROMANS 12:12

But I know, somehow, that only when
it is dark enough can you
see the stars.
        —MARTIN LUTHER KING, JR.

We pass through this world but once.
        —STEPHEN JAY GOULD

Success isn't about how your life
looks to others. It's about how it feels
to you.
        —MICHELLE OBAMA

WHEN THE BRAKES FAIL

A Memoir by
CINDY WITTSTROM

gatekeeper press™
TAMPA, FLORIDA

WHEN THE BRAKES FAIL

Published by Gatekeeper Press
7853 Gunn Hwy, Suite 209
Tampa, FL 33626
www.GatekeeperPress.com

This is a work of non-fiction. All of the events in the memoir are true to the best of the author's memory.

Library of Congress Control Number: 2023934659

ISBN (paperback): 9781662938283
eISBN: 9781662938290

always…
keep searching
for the
Light

CONTENTS

PROLOGUE

We have all been tapped on the shoulder before. It's a nagging little irritation that we would like to ignore, but we can't. We must direct our attention to the cause of the tap. That's where I am—knowing I have to take some action with this tap. It's been haunting me for roughly forty years, and it's time to face it head-on.

This is my story, something I feel I must write. It is uncomfortable and, most likely, won't be a bestseller, but it's my story nonetheless. I take full responsibility for its contents. For the most part, I have lived my life honorably and with as much dignity as I could muster. But it has taken a turn that I did not expect.

I have put pen to paper many times and have compiled journal upon journal, scraps and bits of "relevant" papers, various articles, even portions of this book, but never an organized effort of compilation. Organization has always been my strong suit, but piecing together my scattered life has been overwhelming.

What I *can* say with assurance is that I am dreadfully afraid of *not* writing this book. The clock is ticking. The reason for my procrastination comes from fear—fear of embarrassment, fear of unworthiness, fear of unacceptance, and most importantly, fear of the unknown. I've got this secret, you see, a secret that few people know. It is my "flaw." This "flaw" has proven to be both beautiful and painful. It has given me an understanding of the mental health community, about which I once knew very little.

There is a real possibility that I might face further alienation and backlash from my family. *My* truth about my journey may not be *their* truth about my journey. Recollections and memories twist and fade over the years and, most likely, that has been the case. In no way is this story intended to hurt or embarrass anyone. It is simply my story, my truth, and my discovery.

My only hope is that you, as my reader, will be patient with me. Read this with your heart, with an openness to learn a different story. My story, or something similar, is shared by many, and mostly we suffer in silence. The first utterance that we are suffering may take years to unveil. So this suffering becomes overwhelming, almost deafening.

Mental illness casts a wide net. It encompasses ADHD, social anxiety, schizophrenia, bipolar illness, depression, and postpartum depression. Those afflicted come from all walks of life.

There are two reasons that I am writing this book. The first is that I am searching for clarity and understanding, verifying the dates of events, reviewing my personal expressions via my journals, and finally, learning the effects my illness has had on others, especially those close to me. Secondly, I hope to educate you, the public, on this illness through my life experiences.

There is an excitement for me as well. Unlike other times in my life, I *want* to share these years with you. I have held on, painfully gripping the moments, for far too long. These memories and desires have been held in silence, in secret, up until now. I'm venturing forth into a new world of openness, a world I hope will be productive for both you and me.

As a society we have an obligation to understand this thing we have named mental illness. Part of the reason that the sufferers of mental illness are silent about their pain is shame, real shame. The illness is not regarded as an "illness" because it is unseen, often misinterpreted and overlooked. There is a real shame of unworthiness that sets us apart from others. The brain is the most complex organ in our bodies and probably the most misunderstood. All of our brains are unique and, therefore, problematic to diagnose and treat.

In this book I will attempt to humanize these conditions. I am an average woman, with an average life, who lives with bipolar illness. My life can be complicated, but it can also be beyond beautiful. Reach out your arms, and read my story.

1
A PRETTY PERFECT
CHILDHOOD

So that you may know me a little better, you probably need to understand my roots and my family heritage. I was born into a family of two parents and an older sister, Nanci. There was great excitement with my arrival, as there were eight years between my sister and I. There was never a question as to whether I was loved; it was a given.

We were a working-class family; both parents had to work. My mom worked fifteen miles north at the nearby army training base, Camp Roberts, and my dad was a milk tester at Harmony Valley Creamery in San Luis Obispo. My parents would rotate childcare shifts, so a babysitter was never needed.

Dad always had a side job: breaking colts, jockeying race horses, raising drop calves—whatever he could do to supplement his paycheck. In fact, most of the time, he worked *many* side jobs. He was hardworking, as was my mom. Both of my parents came from poor circumstances. My dad was a first-generation American of Swiss-Italian descent, and my mom was a Depression-era baby from a broken home. They were determined to give my sister and I a better life.

My grandfather, Arnoldo Battista Carminati, and my grandmother, Guiseppina Cattaneo, were from a region in northern Italy and southern Switzerland. It was important to them to be called "Swiss-Italian," *not* Swiss and *not* Italian. Nono, as we called him, was born in Gudo, Italy, and arrived in the California Central Coast area in 1908. Guiseppina, whom we called Nona, was born in St. Antonio, Switzerland, and immigrated to San Miguel in 1915. In 1928, they purchased their North River Road ranch outside of Paso Robles. It was a grape-and-grain operation at the time, but Nono soon changed it into a dairy operation, similar to their farms back home. When he first arrived in America, Nono made charcoal in the Willow Creek area and slept in a tent at the Paso Robles Cemetery. Nona sold eggs to the Poultry Cooperative Association and gathered print-colored sacks so that she could make clothing for her five children. I was lucky enough to gather eggs, play with cousins, and just have fun on the ranch.

Nono, Nona and children at the family dairy farm c. 1932

There were enormous highs and lows on my father's side of the family. Swiss-Italians are known to be excitable. At family parties, there would always be swinging arms, loud storytelling, and lots of hugging. Tears of both sorrow and joy were readily expressed—always entertaining, always fun.

The Veach side of my family was quite different. My mom was raised in Bradley, California, twenty minutes north of Paso Robles. Basically, all my maternal relatives hail from that tiny town. They were a close-knit family, always sharing housing and food. During the hard times, families never lost their houses or missed a meal, and they knew how to conserve. The camaraderie was actually unique, as evidenced by Christmas gatherings, family picnics, and the annual Easter family reunion.

My summers were spent in this small town, where I chased my cousins and attempted to dodge the red fire ants. Bradley was only a small blip on the radar, hardly a metropolis with maybe a population of 1000.

Even though there was a fair amount of traffic from the highway, our freedom was not deterred. We basically had the run of the town, mainly on our bikes. There was that community protectiveness—everyone looked out for everyone. If a motorcycle gang barreled through town, all kids were rounded up and a headcount ensued. Never did quite understand why everyone was so frightened.

The Veach family knew how to have good old-fashioned fun! Parties always included a goofy theme, a schedule of events, decorations, and costumes. Games were aplenty: horseshoes, fishing tournaments, and card games (such as blackjack, poker, and Pedro). It was assumed that all of the family would attend, and you would be sorely missed if you skipped out.

One of my mom's lucrative endeavors was the Big Orange, a respite for thirsty travelers. The round building was made a stucco and painted orange. She served hand-squeezed lemonade and orange juice. Since the old Highway 101 went through Bradley, she served many a glass.

Grandma Alta, Cindy and sister Nanci at the Big Orange, Bradley, CA, 1955

Our house was the "open house" on the block, a gathering place for all kinds of guests. There were the neighborhood kids, Mom's army soldiers from work, teenage employees, and the list goes on. Dad loved to hunt and fish practically anything that moved—deer, elk, trout, and abalone. Mom was the consummate listener who was always game for a little fun. Practical jokes were the norm, and everyone knew they could make Mom howl with laughter.

I was strongly encouraged to succeed in school, and I did. My parents provided me with anything that might help me in school—books, paper, pens, anything. Because they only possessed a high school education, they hoped that I would achieve more. As I began to excel, there was talk of my attending college. Not knowing exactly where the funds would be coming from for higher education, my dad started a cow-and-calf herd so that the funds would be available. He would joke about the cows attending college. Ultimately, I earned scholarships and the funds were never needed.

The notions of hard work and determination are woven throughout our family history. In the past days, you worked hard for everything you had. Having been products of the Great Depression, my parents' life choices were measured and conservative. We never bought anything on credit and we only had a mortgage on our home. If the refrigerator went out, you had better have extra money set aside for a replacement. And you certainly never replaced something that wasn't broken. These values were modeled to the next generation; it was a declaration of sorts.

Ruminating about my family opened up questions in my mind. Since mental illness is most likely genetic, where did I fit into the mix? And from which side of the family did my mental illness originate?

In those days, doctors were rarely visited and no medications were prescribed, so you just suffered from your ailments. I don't know if psychiatrists were even available for mental illnesses. Basically, there is not much I know about my family's medical history. Many of the members have passed, and many are estranged, so my story begins at ground zero.

2

MY FIRST ENCOUNTER

He was conceived in the winter of 1978—both planned and wanted. I was twenty-five, and Karl was twenty-eight. It is common practice for schoolteachers to have spring babies, allowing them the entire summer to enjoy their child before the school year begins in the fall. So this was the case for our dear son-to-be. The entire pregnancy was uneventful, and I worked up until two weeks before the delivery.

The delivery was normal, although long, and it was filled with great joy and excitement. Chad completed the family circle. We went home from the hospital, a new family of three, with a bit of trepidation, not knowing what our jobs might entail.

But as the days unfolded, the joy turned into chaos. The baby wouldn't sleep. *I* couldn't sleep. The days became nights, and the nights became days, and still no sleep. I was exceedingly happy: preparing sumptuous meals, vacuuming the front room at 2:00 a.m., expressing my love to all my friends and family, and finally, organizing a card-writing campaign. I loved everyone, and I loved this euphoria. There was much to do and so little time!

Stressors began to surface. Breastfeeding was not all that easy, especially for a hungry young lad. We had attended Lamaze childbirth training prior to Chad's delivery, but the classes did not prepare us for the actual breastfeeding. There were no lactating nurses on hand to demonstrate any techniques, and certainly no aftercare. My pediatrician was a major advocate of breastfeeding, but he did little to encourage me. In fact, he actually pressured me to continue breastfeeding; quitting was not an option. This was just the kind of pressure I did not need. And here I was, a successful woman in most of my endeavors, and I was failing at this "motherhood thing."

Another nagging concern for me was the impending doom of returning to teach. School was to start in the fall and I wasn't ready to leave my dear son; and in my condition, I couldn't possibly function to teach twenty-five students. This dilemma was real . . . oh so real. These stressors kept adding up, kept smothering me. Still . . . no peace, no sleep.

This sleep deprivation is a serious condition that can cause a myriad of problems, including delirium and hallucinations. The brain doesn't interpret information clearly. My lack of sleep did, in fact, trigger both of these problems. I vividly remember eating at a local diner when I suddenly thought that the other patrons were all looking at and gossiping about me. My husband tried to reassure me that it wasn't the case, but I continued to withdraw. The most frightening experience happened on a trip to our newly purchased rural property. My husband wanted us to have a nice outing, so we went for a hike. There was a canyon in the back of the property, and I was convinced that he brought me there to shoot me. I begged for my life.

Karl regards this incident as the most frightening of all my manic episodes. The fact that I would accuse him of something so sinister was so unlike my personality. He concluded that something was really wrong. Of course, there was no merit to my thought process, but it was so real for me.

One saving grace was my family, with their steadfast love and constant willingness to help. We lived next door to my parents and they would pop in several times a day, just checking to see if we needed them. Sometimes it would be for a minute, sometimes it would be for hours; whatever we needed. They would visit at our house or take the baby to theirs, whatever we needed. But even with all this help, I still could not sleep.

Not knowing what to do, I called my OB-GYN, a prominent elderly physician from San Luis Obispo. He had the answer. He told me to *walk*. So I walked . . . and I walked. No improvement. The walking actually sped up my metabolism, and I became more agitated and still could not sleep. After about a week or two of this madness, we went to our general practitioner, a local small-town doctor. He made the diagnosis almost immediately—postpartum depression.

Mayo Clinic advises:

The birth of a baby can trigger a jumble of powerful emotions, from excitement and joy to fear and anxiety. But it can also result in something you might not expect—depression. Most new moms experience the postpartum "baby blues" condition after childbirth, which commonly includes mood swings, crying spells, anxiety and difficulty with sleeping. "Baby blues" typically begins within the first two or three days after delivery, and may last for up to two weeks. Other new moms experience a more severe long-lasting form of depression know as postpartum depression. Rarely, an extreme mood disorder called postpartum psychosis may also develop. Postpartum depression isn't a character flaw or a weakness.

Sometimes it's simply a complication of giving birth. If you have postpartum depression, prompt treatment can help you manage your symptoms and help you bond with your baby.

Postpartum symptoms can be just as euphoric as depressive. The sheer joy of knowing that you have created another human being is infinitely miraculous. And then witnessing that very creation is beyond words. This euphoric condition can often be tagged as mania.

I cried out for help, and my doctor said to walk! He surely missed the mark. My general practitioner likened my condition to that of a freight train barreling down its tracks, bound for derailment if not stopped. So the only remedy he could suggest was San Luis Obispo County General Hospital, a mental health facility.

Having no inkling of our future, it was arranged for me to voluntarily admit to the psych ward. My world was already fuzzy from lack of sleep, so my health decisions were left up to my husband. These were tough decisions to be made, and he was my best advocate. Uncharted waters for certain.

As we walked beyond the front desk, I entered a world of deafening sounds—screaming, banging, guitar playing, and the clanging of bars, metal bars. It wasn't just a mental health facility; it was a detention facility for all types of mental conditions. I wanted to run . . . this wasn't for me . . .

But for reasons unbeknownst to me, I chose to stay. The swallowing condition of sleeplessness gave me no other choice. San Luis Obispo County General Hospital was my only hope.

3

UNCHARTED WATERS

As a precursor, I must reveal that my memories of this stay are a bit sketchy, with no journals, doctors, or records to consult. Only one record could I procure. On October 14, 1999, I received an answer to my request for medical records. The letter from the Health Agency of the County of San Luis Obispo stated:

> It is the policy of the Community Mental Health Services to destroy records seven years after the date of last contact with clients. You were last seen on 9/11/79 and your records have since been destroyed. The dates of your inpatient stay were 9/6/79 to 9/11/79. We are sorry we were unable to be of more help to you.

However, my impressions, my intuitions, are etched upon my soul. The feelings are crystal clear; therefore, I must rely on these spiritual connections to formulate my interpretations. What I do have are the facts gathered by my family. Very few visitors were allowed in the unit, and frankly, it was probably better that they had to stay away. This was something I had to do alone, something that was mine to conquer.

It was a locked facility—you came in, you didn't come out. The actual intake was voluntary, but the doors were locked once there.

A brief introduction ensued, and I purposely kept trying to separate myself from the moaning old man trying to strip his pants off and the young man tapping on the outside door hoping to be readmitted. He told the staff he was suicidal. It's hard for staff to ignore a possible suicide attempt. The man was savvy enough to know that the staff couldn't ignore his pleas. Most of my possessions were confiscated before I entered the unit: no belt, no purse, no shoes. The mood was chaotic, and I remember the noise, the constant barrage of sounds. And at night, how was I supposed to sleep?

Hell no! I came here to sleep, and this is what you give me?

I was assigned to a double "cell," and I was alone at first. But during the night, a roommate was brought to my room. As luck would have it, the person was a volatile drug user with whom I went to high school. I was so scared that I curled into a ball, trying to disappear into the blankets. Maybe she wouldn't recognize me or see that I was afraid. Coming from a loving, fairly controlled environment, it was frightening.

My initial impression was that the facility was not therapeutic but a sinkhole, a small warehouse, a last resort, a revolving door for most of its patients. It actually proved to be just the case. And blindly, I just willingly jumped on the bandwagon.

There wasn't much time. There was a limit on the number of days available for housing and a limited number of beds. As in most county hospitals, the number of psychiatrists was limited, as was their time. Time was money at these general hospitals, and I was at the mercy of this political dilemma. This fact allowed little or no time for therapy or discussion. The facility's focus was on which medications would be the most suitable for me. Since I had no history of mental illness, it made the doctor's job a bit more difficult. He was basically dealing with a blank slate. The initial diagnosis of postpartum depression seemed to be correct, so the doctor proceeded from there.

Later, my husband referred to this as the "mental health black hole." The doctor would need to "eighty-six" a patient in order to restart the brain. "Eighty-six" is a slang term that means getting rid of a problem and starting completely over. At first there was a medication for my lack of sleep, then a medication for the mania. Because my stay on the unit would be short, there was not enough time for the doctors to analyze. With the drugs lithium and Depakote, my "switch" had been flipped, and I began to feel a change in my behavior and sleep patterns. The trick was to correct the problem without overmedicating the patient.

At the time, Dr. Merna McMillan, a family friend, was the director of Mental Health Services of San Luis Obispo County. She purposely did not visit patients she knew personally, but she did keep an eye out by making frequent visits to the unit. It was a great relief to us, especially to Karl, to know that she was keeping us on her radar during my stay.

About three months ago, during a telephone interview with me, she expressed her concerns regarding our county's mental health crisis. County funding remains a real concern for most counties. Budgeting is always tight at the county level, often leaving mental health departments short on funds. During Dr. McMillan's tenure at San Luis Obispo County General Hospital, there was a sliding scale for patients' fees. She believes that mental health services should not be politicized; however, it is often the case. It is the health department's plan to assess the patient's problems and to return the patient to his community, to his home, as quickly as possible. In most cases, medication is dispensed. Dr. McMillan's primary concern is the lack of services for the mental health community—the lack of in-patient units, the shortage of psychiatrists, and the ineffectiveness of medical insurance. There is a large portion of our society that does not receive essential services. A joint effort must be made by all of the players regarding mental health. All must get on board and make clear and concise decisions.

I was one of the fortunate few. I had enough money, and I had a proactive family. I did not have to languish in the system. After five days, I emerged from this unknown world of chaos with the promise of being a new person, a new Cindy. On the one hand, I was new, but a different kind of new. My brain had been traumatized, although we didn't know how or to what extent. Prior to my stay I was not a drug abuser (or a drinker), but now I was a pill-popper. I despised taking the pills, but I knew that if I missed a dosage, I might regress to the sleepless, crazy state that I had left. Trust was an issue: I didn't trust myself. The self-reliant, self-assured person was gone. At this point I had to rely on everyone else for transportation, for self-care, and most importantly, for childcare. The road ahead was not going to be easy.

I was discharged to a local psychiatrist who seemed adequate, and I remained in his care for roughly a year. From that point, I did not need to take medication, and I found that talk therapy was ineffective. I requested a leave of absence from my local elementary school, and it was granted. This seemed to bring me some relief, knowing that I could have some time to regroup. And regroup, I did.

I was released from the psych unit on September 11, 1979, and on September 20, 1979, I enrolled at Cal Poly, a state university about thirty miles south of home. I needed certain classes to secure a clear teaching credential. Working full time made it next to impossible to take any classes. I thought I would give it a try since I was not working. Remarkably, if you do the math, it was a short period of time between my hospital visit and resuming my education. That is how quickly my brain recovered. I took six units of continuing education and excelled in the classes (the trauma obviously proved to be minimal). A family friend, Bing, babysat Chad while I attended school, and the family continued to rally around me. I was totally mindful of my rest and tried to lead a healthy, productive life. Everything basically returned to normal.

The three and a half months that had elapsed since the beginning of my illness was an uncontrollable roller-coaster ride for the family, but we had survived. We experienced a new world, one that was so foreign. We became a part of a segment of society that we had never known. What to make of it? The lessons were substantial, and we needed to be mindful of any warning signs to come.

4

GREAT EXPECTATIONS

Karl was pretty vocal about his wish to have more children. Surely we could manage the postpartum depression if it surfaced again. I was torn between our desire to have a larger family and my fear of postpartum depression. Chad was wonderful, my dream child. A family of three would be just fine. We had already established our family dynamics and routines. Why would we want to chance it?

Chad with his trusty shovel, 1982

"Chance it" meant, why would I want to put myself in the position of my past angst? Postpartum depression was profound and crippling for me. It embodied my person, my soul. The depression was suffocating and overwhelming. In the midst of it, there seemed to be no way out, no escape. Until you are in the middle of this depression, it's hard to grasp. And combined with the birth of a child, it becomes even more complicated.

Questions surface about your ability to continue functioning as a mother, wife, and contributing member of society. My mind was torn. Were people judging me? Was I somehow responsible for this postpartum depression? Was this something I should be able to control? Would people judge me as a poor partner, wife, or mother if I could not control my environment?

I have always been an overachiever, and what people thought of me was always very important. So this desire to please everyone around me was playing against my fears of being tossed back into the dark side, a place I feared because I was not in control.

After much discussion, I relented: we would try for another child. As the possibilities continued to haunt me, I did my best to suppress the fears. The pregnancy was progressing nicely. All my initial doctor visits were uneventful. My weight and my examinations were within the normal range. Everything was right on track.

Unlike the grandfatherly, status-quo OB-GYN that I chose for my first pregnancy, I selected just the opposite for my new OB-GYN. Dr. George Johnson was young and progressive, hailing from USC (word on the street was that he was a "hotshot," a real "up-and-comer"). This doctor was unafraid to seek the counsel of other professionals to solve difficult situations. And thank God for my choice!

Things began to change. The "normal" pregnancy turned "abnormal" at about my sixth month. My outer measurements were askew, much larger than the standard range. Without much explanation, Dr. Johnson ordered an ultrasound. Ultrasounds were uncommon in those days, unlike the standard procedures of today. His remark, when I pressed him, was that he wanted to "rule out twins." I was given the option of an ultrasound appointment later in the day or the following Monday. Knowing that my anxiety level was rising, I opted for later that afternoon. The doctor's office was in San Luis Obispo, so it was silly to drive thirty minutes home and return later.

It is not in my nature to wander aimlessly with no real purpose. My life is fairly measured, with expectations, priorities, and schedules. On this day I had to kill three hours, and so I found myself wandering about, in and out of store after store. And I started making odd purchases—a trinket for this person and a gift for that person. I spoke with some of the shopkeepers—just mindless chatter, not amounting to any real conversations.

Three hours felt like an eternity. The doctor had said, "Rule out twins." It didn't sound like twins were a real possibility. So if not twins, then what? Confusion and dread began to boil. While eating lunch, I became overwhelmed and erupted into tears as I spoke with the waiter. Tears to a waiter? What a kind young man!

My appointment time had come. My anxiety level continued to climb. I put the hospital gown on and hopped onto the exam table. As the technician fiddled with the ultrasound machine, I casually asked him if the scan didn't show twins, what else could my recent abdomen growth show? In his most "official voice," he explained that the baby could be without a mouth, etc. I could hear no more. I froze.

He absently slid the wand over my belly, revealing that it was indeed twins. As he delivered the news, my entire body shook. I sobbed.

I prayed. They were tears of joy and relief, tears that this pregnancy was viable, was normal, was going to be something special.

Our entire circle of family and friends was elated. There were no twins on either side of the family, so this was a pregnancy we would all experience. But two weeks into my sixth month, things began to unravel. Dr. Johnson told me at the beginning that the human body is not built to carry multiple births and the journey might be difficult. I had already experienced a great deal of pain in my back and under my left breast. This indicated there wasn't much room for the two babies. The pain continued throughout the coming days.

My first real complication was the early onset of contractions. Without any undue stress or activity, I would experience the contractions. The doctor immediately put me on bed rest and prescribed ritodrine in pill form every four hours to stop the contractions. If by chance I failed to wake up in the middle of the night, the contractions would begin again. The only time I could venture forth from the bed was to use the bathroom or take a shower. Even when taking a shower, the contractions would commence. Generally, they would subside when I laid down again.

With bed rest, there was an aloneness that I had never felt before. Very few calls, very few visits. How could there be? Everyone had the assignment of babysitting my son, who was only two. He could lie on the bed with me, but no wrestling, only visiting or reading. Most of the time he was farmed out to my mom or my sister. They had their hands full. We had to hire an in-house nanny who could rush me to the hospital if I went into preterm labor. Karl was on duty when the nanny clocked out.

I cherished the calls, the greeting cards, and the sweet notes that people sent to me. I saved each one. I read them over and over again. They gave me encouragement that people were indeed thinking of me. To this day I send lots of cards, knowing how such correspondence touched me. The bed rest gave me empathy for people who are permanently assigned to their beds.

This bed rest also made me aware of the importance of acts of kindness. If you suspect that a person needs comfort, he probably does. It then becomes an action-based trigger on your part. Make your move. Don't procrastinate. Find an opportunity via a card, a call, or a visit. You will really make a difference in someone's life.

I read book after book. I could tell you which character was doing what on every soap opera. My life's day-to-day thoughts and activities shrank in scope, but I knew there would eventually be an end to this misery. My only job was to carry these babies to full term. I had to prevail!

One day my contractions would not stop. The doctor met me at the hospital and began intravenous ritodrine. My head bounced off the pillow as I received this medication. The nurse likened it to "liquid speed," and it somehow reversed the contractions. Apparently, this was a common reaction to this medication. At this point, arrangements were being made to airlift me to Mount Sinai, a hospital with a top-notch neonatal unit.

The intravenous drug continued to be siphoned into my body with the hope that a miracle could halt the craziness. It was maddening, and it was administered for hours. Without warning, the contractions subsided.

Not long after I was released from the hospital, the doctor utilized another procedure to further prepare for the twins' arrival. Betamethasone, a corticosteroid, was injected intramuscularly to mature the fetal lungs. An amniocentesis was then performed to check the effectiveness of this medication by measuring a substance that increases the production of surfactant in the fetal lungs—betamethasone, two injections intramuscularly, twenty-four hours apart, and then repeated two weeks later.

All these measures were repeated in the coming months. I compartmentalized my days one by one. Small tasks, small steps, all in the hopes that I could bring life to these two babies. It was a team effort. I would not ask for the sex of the babies. It would be best if I didn't know. If they weren't viable, I didn't want to fully commit. The heartache would be too great. I didn't want to choose names, and God forbid, I didn't want to envision a nursery. I just led my life blindly, day by day.

5

DOUBLE THE TROUBLE

I must interject that I complied with my doctor's orders. I have always been a rule-follower, and this approach enabled me to turn the focus off me and onto the babies. Somehow my faith enabled me to focus directly on the doctor—only on *his* instructions. If he told me to jump, I would ask, "How high?" My family and friends had their stories to share—the old wives' tales, their opinions on what I should do and how often I should do it. I politely received their suggestions, ignored them, and then deferred to my doctor. He had experienced my situation before, and I was sure he had many success stories. What I am trying to say is that I became laser-focused. We consulted a few other doctors initially, but for the most part, I didn't read many medical journals or consult a handful of doctors. Whatever the doctor said, I did. He was the expert, and I was simply along for the ride.

And the ride finally came. Dr. Johnson felt that the babies' lung surfactant was at an acceptable level, so he had me quit the oral ritodrine. Surfactant is made by the cells in the airways and consists of phospholipids and protein. It begins to be produced in the fetus at about twenty-four to twenty-eight weeks of pregnancy and is found in amniotic fluid between twenty-eight and thirty-two weeks. By about thirty-five weeks gestation, most babies have developed adequate amounts of surfactant.

I assumed I would go into immediate labor, but I thought wrong! I walked back and forth to the barn, but no contractions. It seemed odd to me. Now that I *wanted* contractions, they weren't happening. Finally, the next day, it was time to head to the hospital. I was at thirty-six weeks. Both my OB-GYN and the pediatrician were on full alert. Both were on call throughout the day. Labor was fairly quick, and "Baby A" was born about noon on September 21, 1982—coming in at a whopping six pounds! The pediatrician ran down the corridor with her, her first introduction to the family and friends who had been waiting. I was told that my father exclaimed, "At least we have one." He said what everyone was thinking.

But "Baby B" proved to be more difficult. She had turned breech a couple of days prior to the delivery. An attempt to externally invert the baby into a headfirst position was unsuccessful. A decision to attempt a vaginal breech delivery was agreed upon. Despite Pitocin augmentation of labor for two and a half hours, there was no progression. We agreed to take the baby by cesarean section. "Baby B" was successfully delivered—coming in at a whopping five pounds, fourteen ounces!

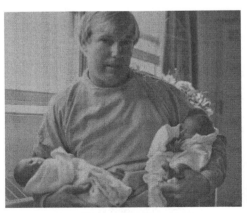

Proud Papa with twins, 1982

I was tired, but the job was complete. Two beautiful baby girls, now named Amanda Karin (Baby A) and Heidi Kathleen (Baby B). Everyone was elated except for my dear Chad, the big brother. When he saw the two pink blankets, he knew they were not boys. Little did he know that both of those "pink" babies would be mighty tomboys. This team of three would be hard to beat in the coming years.

Because both babies were jaundiced, they needed to stay in the hospital for several days. Since I was nursing, the hospital allowed me to stay as a board-and-care patient at no cost other than occupying a room. I did all the other tasks for myself: changing my bedding, retrieving my meals, and bringing the babies to my room to nurse. It was almost a vacation, and it allowed me to care for the babies with relatively no stress. I read several books and visited with my family. We stayed about ten days.

There was a fantastic lactating nurse who spent hours instructing me on how to nurse the twins, and I became adept at nursing them both at the same time. She was so masterful in her teaching skills that I nursed them for seven months without supplementing one bottle! The nursing was a big cost savings and also allowed me more freedom since I didn't have to rotate feedings. I simply nursed them at the same time and then could easily put them down for a nap since both of their tummies would be full.

One day while I was nursing, Dr. Johnson came into my room. He explained that he had been accessing my patient files and learned about my stay at the hospital psychiatric unit three years before. I froze. He was dumbfounded as to why I hadn't explained my medical history to him, especially since it pertained to my postpartum depression.

Dr. Johnson and I developed a plan of action to prevent the recurrence of the same problem. Since lack of sleep and hormonal swings were my triggers, he now knew what to look for. He didn't really understand my shame, my attempt to cover up my inadequacies. I already knew the ropes, how to conceal my weaknesses. But from this point forward, I had the opportunity to be honest and open with a doctor. No longer would I need to conceal my past.

I have found that most of the time, doctors don't really care about your history, let alone your mental health history. You make an appointment, fill out the questionnaire, have a quick exam, pay your bill, and it's over. I usually don't reveal my entire mental health history, my medications, etc. I do not want to make a negative impression or have the doctor prejudge my person. And if I don't broach the subject, I won't be privy to their opinions. The judgment isn't worth the effort.

The focus of our family's energies was on the twins: feeding, bathing, and loving. The saint in all this was my husband. Other than when he was working, he was my right-hand man. At the night feedings he would wake up, change the diapers, bring each baby to me to nurse, and then repeat the process. One night I fell asleep when nursing and woke up frantically, trying to find the baby, and he had already placed her back in the crib. In some ways it was madness, and we just prayed for the courage to keep going.

As time passed, it did get easier. The middle-of-the-night craziness subsided, and the normal activities of rolling, crawling, and walking were fun to watch. We worked at keeping the bedlam to a controlled minimum, but our lives would never be the same.

There is something that has always bothered me about the twins' birth—that is, how it affected our son. There was such attention lavished on the girls, mainly because they weren't singletons. People—even strangers—wanted to compare their looks to each other. Were the girls identical? What were their differences? The attention was fun at first, but it became embarrassing, even bothersome.

And while they fawned over the girls, they overlooked the older child. One time in the grocery store, as a stranger was cooing over the girls, Chad outstretched his hand and said in his most grown-up voice, "Hi, my name is Chad Wittstrom." I could have melted, cried. Our sole focus had been on the girls, simply trying to get by daily, and Chad had suffered. Shame on us. We made some real changes from that point forward.

In case you were curious, there was no sign of postpartum depression following this pregnancy. Maybe it was the mild sleep medication that I was prescribed since a lack of sleep was my trigger. Maybe it had something to do with my hormones. We just don't know.

But we did have a competent gatekeeper in my doctor. He kept my medical progress in check, and I believe he was the difference in this pregnancy. Trust is a huge issue, and I was willing to trust him. We were as prepared as we could be, but the postpartum depression was held at bay. Thank you, God!

6

THE EXPLANATION
OF THE ABSENCE

My life has never run an even course, and this period of my life followed suit. It was measured in absence. From September 1979 until March 1997, there was an absence of any hint of depression or mania. That's a total of eighteen years! It was an important period, a juxtaposition to the tumultuous times of the disease.

What filled this void was hard work, family activities, and peace. This peace was evident as days, weeks, months, and years passed. No longer did I worry that the depression would return. No longer did I worry about the madness. There were no hints.

The years were filled with many activities. As I have listed them on my scraps of paper, I wonder if there were too many, but they seemed important at the time. Looking back, I wouldn't have changed a thing.

At this point my career was centered on our family business. We owned an oil-field trucking and construction business that later developed into an environmental remediation company. I managed the in-house accounting department, focusing on payroll. We grew slowly but became a solid company. After eighteen years, we eventually sold the company to a Fortune 500 company and we phased out after our employment contracts expired. I had mixed emotions about the sale. Many of the employees were friends: we celebrated babies and marriages together. But the sale gave us the opportunity to rid ourselves of possible liability lawsuits. Within the hazardous materials business, there is always a chance of a spill or an incorrect analysis.

At the time of the sale we had four locations and roughly two hundred employees. I managed the payroll and the human resources departments while still supervising the accounts payable and receivables. Payroll weeks could not be missed. Frankly, I don't know how this was possible, especially with raising three children.

Our kids' active lives kicked into gear as they each enjoyed the years of preschool at the old War Memorial Hospital, which had been converted. There was a lot of history at this location. I was even born there. There were many daily trips, to and fro, but I felt it was important that they experienced the social and educational interaction. I also encouraged play dates with other children. The kids liked to entertain their friends at our home, and everyone seemed to enjoy the country activities on our property.

The kids' elementary school teachers encouraged parents to visit and assist in classroom activities. I helped in all three of the children's classes for six years, kindergarten through fifth grades, and got to know their friends and, of course, their teachers. Knowing which kids were kind, troubled, or good students was valuable in many ways. These days were joyful but required much of my time. As the kids progressed in age, I became not as needed in the classroom. Typical teenagers don't want Mom around their friends. So I focused my energies on PTA and held the office of treasurer for a number of years. It was my role in the family to help with homework, and it proved to be a never-ending chore, but we plugged ahead.

Church was a large part of our lives, and we missed few Sundays. I coordinated Vacation Bible School for many years. In my final year we reached one hundred kids by combining three nearby churches. As our kids got older, Karl and I became youth group leaders, always devising activities. We would go boating at Lake Nacimiento, always praying that our old gray boat would start. Many a time we had to be towed, but no one complained; the kids were just happy to be doing something different.

Our kids were always involved in sports: T-ball, football, basketball, softball, gymkhana, and roping. I was the driver and the cheerleader, and Karl was usually the coach. Lots of time, lots of fun. Because we lived in the country, the kids did "country stuff." They all had their horses, some they had raised as foals. They devised "jumps" in the arena and rode to the neighbors' place, the Wallers, to rope. They competed in local team ropings and gymkhanas—too many to count. If their dad would trailer the horses, they were eager to attend.

The kids met a local dairyman who was willing to sell them any male Holstein drop calf that he didn't want. They paid him a nominal fee and brought the calves home to bottle-feed. They consistently bottle-fed the calves morning and night for approximately three months without a change in schedule. Never a whine or complaint. When the calves were mature enough to pasture, they would be put into the fields and, when large enough, later sold. The kids did this time and again, earning good little nest eggs.

They loved almost any animal. Heidi would tame feral cats and sit for hours in the barn, coaxing them to eat food. Amanda had one of her horses trained to come on demand with her whistle. Chad excelled at roping, which was remarkable because he was left-handed but learned to rope with his right hand.

We also loved camping at the Indians. The area was located by Jolon and Mission San Antonio. It was difficult to find, so there were very few people. There were waterholes with giant boulders—such fun for swimming! Lots of hiking and exploring. Food packing was always a chore since you only had what you packed. One time we came home early since we ran out of ketchup for our fried potatoes at breakfast. No, really, it was such fun.

During this time, I felt I was called to help at a local food bank, Loaves and Fishes. The organization "specializes in serving the working poor, the elderly living on a fixed income, those with physical limitations, and young parents trying to make ends meet—by helping with groceries and other necessities." I worked as both an interviewer of clients and as a bookkeeper for probably eight years or so. It was a learning curve for me because I had never been exposed to hunger or insufficiency and had never missed a meal.

Another group that I became involved with was Cursillo. It is a nondenominational program, a short course in Christianity. It is a three-day retreat organized by laypeople. Ours was held at the San Miguel Mission, built in the 1700s. The sheer holiness of the site was a blessing to all who attended. The Cursillo movement was designed to deepen the spiritual life and bring about Christian involvement in daily activities. Cursillo provided me with the opportunity to grow in my faith and discover my relationship with God with other participating women.

San Miguel Mission, late 1700s

This time of absence from depression, this relief from the madness, gradually became a given. While the period of absence was wonderful and filled with great joy, we often wondered if the turmoil might return. It appeared that we had held it at bay. Eighteen years had been a long, fruitful time . . .

7

THE RED SUIT

It came like a slow-rolling California earthquake—basically un-predictable, with little warning. That is how it began for me.

That year I applied to the San Luis Obispo County Grand Jury. It is a civil grand jury, which operates as a "watchdog" for our county's citizens. The jury investigates citizen concerns and reports on the operation of local government. There are nineteen volunteer community members impaneled by the Superior Court judges.

An annual report is generated by the jury and the investigated agency must respond to all the report's concerns. Up until the reports are completed, the information is confidential. The scope of the investigations can include inspecting and auditing expenditures of county agencies, inspecting records of special districts, examining any nonprofit receiving county or city funds, inquiring into the condition of jails and detention centers, and inquiring into any charges of willful misconduct of public officials or employees.

Needless to say, the position could be dicey. We had the power to subpoena certain records, and we were not the most well-liked agency in the county. A juror was selected by a Superior Court judge and could be "held over" for a subsequent year.

It was fascinating work, and it was basically a full-time job. The office was in San Luis Obispo, our county seat. Since my husband and I sold our business, I was looking for something interesting to do. This is where I chose to hang my hat in 1996 and 1997.

The sitting Superior Court judge selects the foreman who, in turn, appoints a vice chairman. The secretary is provided by the county office. I was initially appointed as vice chairman but was advanced to foreman due to the original appointee's illness.

Decisions were made by consensus. If all members failed to vote in the affirmative, then the issue would be dismissed. These decisions encompassed deciding which complaints to investigate, the specifics on the scope of the investigation, and the final reports at year end. We always worked in teams of at least two jurors.

All went well for the first year and for the majority of the second year. As we began finalizing the lengthy reports in year two, a juror began to express her displeasure with the findings. Try as we might, it quickly became clear that she would not vote with the consensus. Our committees had spent most of the year creating some of these reports that were now going to be negated by this one juror. The frustration was growing for the entire jury, especially for me, since I was the juror in charge.

I do not handle conflict well. I internalize my feelings, and then they present themselves in a myriad of ways. But these manifestations were different. I began to talk incessantly and sleep little, and I lost fifteen pounds. People began to ask if I was ill. Other than the weight loss, I didn't see the changes.

Amid the grand jury turmoil, my uncle passed away. Of course, it was sad, but I felt conflicted. There had always been bad blood between my uncle and my father—stemming from things that transpired *years* ago. Of course, my loyalty was always with my father, but my heart ached for my uncle's immediate family. This uncle had lost two daughters from leukemia when they were teenagers, so his family knew pain. This we all understood.

My uncle's death exacerbated the family drama. Prior to his death, trouble had been brewing. A deep chasm had formed within the family when the grandparents died. The divide was mostly over money and property, a common occurrence among families. It became so intense that half of the siblings sued the rest of the siblings, challenging the existing will. Extravagant claims were made, sides were chosen, and my dad suffered greatly.

He was both angry and embarrassed. I witnessed his soulful hurt, something I had never seen before. He had always been a right-and-wrong, black-and-white guy, so this complicated mess was a nightmare. Because we have always been close, I suffered with him with feelings I had never experienced. These emotions were so foreign. I am the type of person who tries to understand both sides of an issue, and this turmoil was confusing to me.

I believe that my dad suffered some sort of nervous breakdown because of the family unrest. We felt it necessary to remove his guns from the house, not knowing what he might do. He homesteaded our house for fear the other side of the family might take it away. Ultimately, the judge ruled in favor of my dad and his brother, but the damage had been done. To this day, grudges remain, and generations of our family do not know each other. I find this shameful, but we are all human, each with our own frailties.

All the unrest and pain, combined with the grand jury fiasco, proved to be more than I could handle. Due to the confidentiality laws, I could not talk about the jury difficulties. Since family loyalties could not be discussed, I suffered in silence. The outside world was eating away my inside world.

My friend, Ann, who had witnessed my slow decline and frustration, suggested that I see her doctor for an evaluation as her doctor was more progressive than mine. I knew that something wasn't right with me, but I didn't know what it was. I had been at the grand jury's office all morning but needed to drive back to Templeton to keep the doctor's appointment.

People have described anxiety attacks to me, but I had never experienced one. I drove from work to the doctor, and my car's radio miraculously played one of my favorite songs, "Neon Moon" by Brooks and Dunn. I sang at the top of my lungs, hoping to stay focused on the road. I knew every word and I let it consume me, to channel my thoughts. My heart pounded and my head throbbed. Upon arrival, the nurse shuttled me into an examination room. My friend must have alerted them to my condition. I began to cry, sobbing to complete strangers, and I was desperate for a solution, anything, hoping this doctor could help. She did help the best way she could have: she called French Hospital.

None of my family was available for the transport. Most were at our family reunion at the lake, and cell phones had limited range. The next best solution was transport by ambulance. Leave the car in the parking lot and let them take you. Release your will, release your power. Do it solo.

There are angels among us, and two of my angels that day were the ambulance crew. They held my hands and told me comforting answers to my frightful questions. They knew; everyone knew . . . but me.

When the ambulance arrived at the hospital, I got out on my own accord. There I stood in a bright-red seersucker business suit with a mandarin collar. To the general public, I didn't appear to be in trouble, but I was quickly whisked away to an exam room.

I completed the necessary paperwork, or partly completed it. There were so many questions and I did not know the answers. It seemed like an eternity, but as I was staring at a small bird nest decoration, Dr. Nancy Speed walked into the room. Unassuming and mildly friendly, she asked a lot of questions and patiently waited for my answers. She was assessing me, I knew that. I tried to be as open and as honest as I could be. But I was becoming more and more confused, and my head was continuing to ring. If only I knew what she was thinking.

I gave her permission to treat me, to heal me, whatever it took. That's when I was admitted to the French Hospital Psychiatric Unit. It was March 27, 1997.

8

TICKTOCK

For some strange reason, I felt safe. Maybe no more searching, no more exhaustion. A familiar-looking nurse came to me. I recognized her from Cursillo. She sat with me as I chattered away. Because of our connection, she asked if perhaps I wanted a Bible as a means of comfort.

"Of course," I said. It seemed like I read verse after verse of comfort and peace for hours. I stayed up all night, and sleep never came.

I was "off the radar" for twelve or so hours. No one knew where I was (cellular reception wasn't what it is now). The hospital eventually reached my husband. Initially, the phones were inaccessible, or so I thought. The two phones were attached to a wall and were only available for calling card calls or collect calls. I certainly couldn't remember my card number and didn't want to bother anyone with a collect call. Later on, during my stay, I could remember my calling card number, but I only made a few calls as they were discouraged.

The unit was a locked facility, and visitors were basically discouraged. We had a visitors' list of about five people, which could be adjusted daily. The visits were scheduled infrequently. If a visitor upset me, their visits would be terminated. Actually, *I* once frightened a visitor since my behavior was erratic. It probably wasn't in my best interest to have visitors anyway. The visitors on my list were my husband, my parents, and a friend who was in the medical field.

My college-aged son, Chad, insisted on a visit at one point. The visit was distressing and really shouldn't have occurred. Karl said the family was actually "shell-shocked" and didn't know what to expect on a daily basis. Chad's visit was probably the most shocking. He was immediately taken aback by my weight. He thought I weighed about ninety-eight pounds and appeared disheveled. My hair was not done, and I was anxious to show him my drawings. The drawings were in crayon since we were not able to use markers or pens. He felt that my illness did not warrant a locked facility and the other patients had much more difficult situations than his mother. When he went to the Easter family reunion to talk to his grandmother and sisters, he broke down, sobbing and sobbing. The entire ordeal was really too much for children to have to endure.

The girls were thirteen when I went into the hospital. Not only did *we*, as parents, not know how to handle it; *they*, as children, were confused. I lost credibility in their eyes, and that has lasted for years. Our son couldn't understand, just like it was hard for me to understand. The only difference was that I had a mission—to get well—whatever it took.

My sister, Nanci, visited me in spirit daily. She had a single white rose delivered each day, and so I began to share them with the other patients. It was an act of kindness that I treasured. Somehow, during the admissions process, I ended up with only a few clothes. Dr. Dave, our dear friend, had privileges at French Hospital and stopped by daily. His wife, Debi, kept me in clean clothes. Most of my clothing did not fit since I had lost so much weight. My well-being took on a team approach. I was covered in prayers, and there was hope that all my earthly needs would be met.

The unit's primary objective was to observe and then treat its patients. Each patient was diagnosed independently. Trying to co-ordinate approximately twelve to fifteen patients must have been maddening. There were all sorts of patients, from all walks of life. As I began to regain some of my bearings, I came to know residents suffering from conditions such as clinical depression, psychosis, agora-phobia, and of course, bipolar illness. One young fellow was admitted as a 5150, "harmful to self or others." He confided that he was detained because he shoved a revolver into his mouth in front of the officers. God only knows his motivation! We spent hours together playing ping-pong. On the surface he seemed like such a sweet, average kid.

There were many people, many dilemmas, and we all needed help and didn't know where to go for it. Somehow we all landed at French Hospital and were willing to take our chances.

As I remember, the unit was quite large, and it accommodated both individual and group counseling. There was a recreation area, a dining hall, and a drug dispensary. My room was white and stark, with two twin beds and a small bathroom with only a toilet and sink. Communal showers were available only with permission, and only at certain times. Our safety was the priority on the unit. Razors and all items containing alcohol were prohibited. The facility avoided suicide attempts at all costs.

In the main hall there was a large medical-type clock that recorded the seconds, minutes, and hours. It was my lifeline to normalcy. The ticktock sound was actually comforting. The thinking in my head would cease as long as I listened to the sound. It also marked the time for receiving medication.

It was commonplace for the patients to experience physical ailments as well. Headaches and body aches were some of the concerns we had. I had a terrific headache, which was understandable. My neck and back were also sore. Sometimes extra tests were prescribed to rule out physical ailments. This allowed the physician to eliminate any other malady that might exist. Many of the symptoms were caused by stress, and if they were treatable by over-the-counter medications, these were dispensed by the nurses.

I can remember requesting medications too frequently and being disappointed when I was denied. This dispensary process was another mechanism that required our accountability: watch the clock, be patient, and develop an awareness of each drug taken. It was especially difficult for me since my medications and dosages changed almost daily.

Somehow the staff kept close contact with all of us, especially when there could be triggers between patients. On one occasion in the dining room, I apparently irritated another patient. In my manic state I was chatting it up with other patients, and the other patient snapped. She told me to shut up or she would kick my butt. Staff immediately defused the situation and I returned to my room, not really understanding what had happened. The gal was no doubt violent, and I wanted no part of it.

There were two residents per room and, due to my lengthy stay, I had two different roommates. In a way it was reminiscent of camp. You always had a go-to friend. My first roommate was a well-educated, personable gal with a personality similar to mine. She had a loving family that was prominent in the community. She left the unit when her insurance benefits expired, and I was sad to see her go. We still exchange Christmas cards, and I am so appreciative of her kindness.

My next roommate was quite the opposite of me. She was quiet, pensive, and afraid of her shadow. She confided to me that she was agoraphobic. Most of her life she was holed up in her house, afraid to venture out into the world. I often wondered how she maneuvered. She was college-educated and, I think, a librarian. At the time of intake, she did book translations. She had a very soothing voice. Because the doctor was experimenting with my drug regimen, I had problems with my vision. I could not make out newspaper text, only the headlines; and so Frances, who had a soothing voice, would read the paper to me. Our roles were reversed; she talked, I listened. We made an unusual team, but it worked.

We both shared a love of church. It was Easter, which I had forgotten during this craziness. My husband arranged for our pastor to bring Holy Communion to us. He came to the unit as a visitor, and Frances and I shared this priceless moment together. We kept in touch until her death.

I have never been a drug user, so it made the doctor's job a little easier. When other recreational drugs are mixed with therapeutic drugs, it can often be a challenge. For me, it was simply trial and error—a little of this, a little of that, or sometimes a combination of drugs. Dr. Speed was basically treating me for my mania. While some drugs would paralyze me, others actually increased my mania, and some did absolutely nothing. There were some drugs that needed to be in your system for a certain length of time, so you had to wait for its maximum result. This was all time-sensitive and was the reason that my stay was the maximum number of days. My brain had been traumatized and it would take time to heal.

One drug in particular literally sent me to my knees, and I could not walk. Needless to say, this drug was discarded. Toward the end of my stay, I was definitely more stable. The entire process had been an exploration of the unknown, and Dr. Speed's experimentation paid off.

Dr. Speed was a plodder, a rock, a friend. We shared a trust that I have never known with another human being. She was my ally and my confidant for thirteen years. She knew my fears, my turmoil, and my frustrations. She also learned of my love and appreciation for family and for life in general.

9

MY WANDERINGS

My doctor encouraged journaling, which I learned can help me control my symptoms and improve my mood. It helps me to prioritize problems, fears, and concerns. The writings can help you plan, add to your self-care routine, and promote gratefulness. These thoughts may also be helpful for your doctor by providing him with useful information. The actual entries are usually off-limits for sharing with others, unless the patient chooses to reveal its contents. Triggers can also be tracked through journaling. Your thoughts are never wrong; scribbles and doodles are always accepted. Anything is okay.

In my situation, journaling provided me with dates of entry, behavioral changes, and constructive time management. It is important to journal on a regular basis and create a deliberate routine. These journals are the focus of this chapter—specifically, my entries during my stay at French Hospital. They are unaltered, without edit. Some entries may seem disjointed, but remember that a variety of drugs were being pumped through my system. My thoughts were often clouded by the illness. On the other hand, yearnings for a better life were crystal clear. Some entries may even appear childlike or lofty. My hope is that you will have a better understanding of me and the bipolar illness as well.

The staff of the unit would choose a quotation or theme for the day and then we would have the opportunity to comment in our journals. You, as the reader, will not see certain characteristics of the entries. These include the size of my handwriting, the slant of letters, additional doodles, jumbled unintelligible thoughts, line spacing, and words written on top of other words. Noticeable visual changes in my journaling occurred when my medications were changed.

March 21, 1997
(NO THEME)
....
Matthew, Mark, Luke, John had good news and passed it on . . . I laid on the floor, awaiting his morning awakening, for I could hardly contain my emotions. He needed to know how much I loved him. I pressed my back to the wall just as I had before I gave birth to my real twins, Amanda and Heidi. I wanted him to know that I was anxiously awaiting his rebirth—I have laid in wait for him for an eternity. I must be patient and let him rest. I now understand it all, I think, for maybe only to me, maybe for the world. The only thing I know for sure is that he has suffered enough and has risen and I have received the confirmation that good has once again prevailed.

March 22, 1997
THEME: "WILDFLOWERS: Don't care where they grow."
....
My Rebirth, My Homecoming, My Life, My Life. Minnie Pearl wears flowers on her hat. Vicki gave this most wonderful shirt to me—a real gift, given unselfishly, somewhat like the gifts of the Lord. Three with roses symbolize: The Trinity (Father, Son, and Holy Ghost) Purity. Three beautiful children—Chad, Amanda and Heidi. Three adult women—Betty, Nanci, Cindy.

Mom, Nanci and Cindy camping at the lake, 1984

Wildflowers are beautiful because they are grown naturally, beautiful simply because. I guess kind of like all of God's children, even me. Surprises continue to unfold. Yet, the only real surprise is that all these surprises are no surprise to the sweetest Father of the World. Ann's gift to me, Victoria is full of flowers also. I am beginning to understand how visual I actually am. I love the magazine and will subscribe to it. When we redecorate (Nanci, Karl for consultation, Will and I) we can refer to some of these pictures for ideas.

I love all flowers, even weeds. I took a wildflower class at Cal Poly and loved learning about them. Someone wrote on my journal, "live your day as fully as you can as you never know what tomorrow will bring."

Sunday, March 23, 1997

THEME: *"The Dance of Spring is the Dance of Life. Sometimes awful things have to happen for beautiful things to occur."*

Dancing can entice, enhance and excite the senses. Music goes deep within the depths of one's soul, rhythmically connecting the brain's electrodes and sensory systems. Cause and effect of the Good and the Evil and the hideous and beautiful of the World, as we know it. Let's Fox Trot, Waltz, Cha Cha, and 2 Step. I want to dance with my friend, my lover, my confidant, my Karl.

Sunday, March 23, 1997

(NO THEME)

Earthly angels are flying in formation like the way birds fly in the v-pattern, supporting one another. We are like angels to each other like the birds. Suzie is an earthly angel with her struggles.

Sunday, March 24, 1997

THEME: *"Everyone can be GREAT. You only need a heart full of grace and a soul generated by LOVE."*

A sprinkling of grace touches our hearts and enriches our lives, just like Marjie and her precious sign language. Greatness comes in many forms—but money can often destroy the grace of greatness. Greatness comes from the gift of loving freely, unabashedly, without a fear of reprisal. Souls are generated by LOVE—for without love we would not have a soul. We set our own limits, but God does not set limits upon our greatness. Sometimes only age and wisdom go hand in hand—the young often cannot understand their greatness potential. But some youngsters can be wise sages as well.

Tuesday, March 25, 1997

THEME: *"Today is the first day of the rest of our days/lives."*

This seems so easy, so simple, so silly almost, but it is so true. They said visit me when I am alive, never when I am dead. Death is only a resurrection of life, not an ending, but a beginning. Renzo's death brought me hope of a new life, of that new beginning of unknown relatives, resolved disputes, opportunities of love in new forms. I choose life, not death, because of all of the blessings I have received. I have also understood others do not have these blessings and they are very foreign to them. To the point where they almost destroy themselves because of their pain. Do not judge others lest ye be judged—you need to walk in another man's shoes before you can make assumptions. Mr. Mark signed my journal.

Wednesday, March 26, 1997

THEME: *"To enjoy the day to the best of our ability!!!"*

That's Betty, my mom. Life is too short to put any time values on it. To assume a person's lifespan is 1 month, 1 year, 10 years or 100 yrs. is simply ludicrous. Love for today for no one knows what tomorrow will bring. Even Christ's love may bring death, just like with Mary and Annette, and with all of the other loved ones which have passed. Enjoyment means: fulfillment, laughter, kindness, a letting go, a fullness of love you can't wait to share, like a new gift, sharing with old, dear friends. A silliness, a new way of looking at an old idea, family, even with its complexities. Non-monetary sacred moments yet even expensive moments are occasionally a blast. Puppies, kitties, church family, communion, knowing the Lord. We can only do the best with what the Lord has given us; although our possibilities are limitless—for we are only bound by new-found art is an example of a latent talent and who would have imagined I had to be at my worst to discover my best?

Thursday, March 27, 1997

THEME: *"Love can fly in on a thistle. And there are many kinds of thistles."*

The wind blows the seeds hither and thither, never knowing whence the seeds will light. Love is so similar, those people come into our lives—some quickly, and some for life. We cannot control their comings and goings and really nor do we wish to. Often love appears coarse, like the Swiss-Italians but they love nonetheless, and should not be compared with the soft, angelic love of my mother and sister. Sometimes the coarsest of love is actually the truest form—unmasked, yet unconditional, like the wind. Thistles are like people, taking all forms—bull thistles, star thistles, but all thistles just the same. There's a hardiness of the thistle which is beautiful. All the spray in the world cannot kill the true love, nor the spiney, bothersome thistles. Hence, thistles are love.

Friday, March 28, 1997

THEME: *"Become your own best friend."*

Best friends are rare, unusual. Sisters, soul sisters, old and new friends. How did I get so lucky to have so many friends? Becoming your best friend isn't always easy—it takes time, a slow process with great allowances for humbleness. Best friends are mutual and are cherished beyond words. B—beyond love; E—Everyone's dream; S—Sacred; T—Tried and true.

Saturday, March 29, 1997

THEME: "Be with others, but be yourself."
....

By being with others it reaffirms yourself, your self-worth, your importance, however these relationships should not "suck you dry" and not allow you to be yourself. Others can offer you a sense of reality, a reality check of sorts. On the other hand, so long as your reality is in check, you need to be yourself, to know who you are—to know who you are—to know where you are going. It's so imperative to know the difference between the two. Others offer a community, a sense of belonging, a sense of love and self-worth, which in turn allows a person to be themselves and to love others in return. In retrospect my community was intact but it was difficult to be myself with my pastor, my husband and my children. I have great faith that all will change rather quickly, especially because of this situation.

Sunday, March 30, 1997 (Easter Sunday)

THEME: The Golden Rule: "Do unto others as you would have them do unto you."
....

I am born again at Easter. Others=You. No barriers, no walls, only love, like Christ's love. "He's Alive" a song sung by Dolly Parton. Simple drawings of: Easter basket, cross, sunrise, and Easter eggs.

Monday, March 31, 1997

THEME: "I knew we had rough days ahead, but I also know that my faith would be more contagious than any disease that would strike our family. I would keep it in my heart and I would display it by my actions."
....

Nothing in life is perfect, for we do not live in a perfect world; even Jesus, although contrary to popular opinion, did not live in a perfect world—and he was crucified by it. But the hope of it all is that He lives on, through the resurrection, and through the Holy Spirit. Diseases and plagues of the earth will sweep the earth, but those too are his plan, his punishment for our not living up to his standards—locusts, frogs, angels of death . . . But he is the most powerful, and with that comes awesomeness—and my faith has been renewed by the Holy Spirit. Thank you, God, for your grace and your abiding, unconditional love.

Tuesday, April 1, 1997

THEME: *"Love one minute at a time."*

One minute, one hour, one day, one month, one year, one decade, one hundred years—each moment we need to love. Time is elusive and we must realize that must not dictate time upon others, for our time is God's time—that others are not capable of regulating time for them, i.e., children, Ryan, SJ, Karl, Mark, Ronnie and Nanci, Mary, Renzo, Mom and Dad, Mary, Ann, Bev, Dawn, Dr. Dave, Pastor Floyd and many others. Time is the great healer—and the greater result is love. My lifelong ambition is that the three special women in my life are healed—N&B&C. There is great hope if we are only willing.

Wednesday, April 2, 1997

THEME: *"As far as possible, without surrender, be on good terms with all people."*

Good terms=Desiderata. Will use this in our new addition, along with Angel poster and calendars of new puppies. "Without surrender"—cannot give yourself up in spite of your other concessions to other people. Be on good terms with all people—good terms, good people, good life, good love, good husband, good children, good parents, good sister, Dr. Dave, good Tami and all other friends. Surrender your nakedness.

Many of my entries included thoughts and dreams concerning my family, especially my mom and my sister. There has always existed a bond that is difficult to explain and, perhaps, understand.

In general, I was later surprised by the repetitious thought patterns of the journal entries. I would be fixed on a particular thought that I couldn't finish, and so I would just draw or repeat words. It must have been grueling to gather the thoughts in an attempt to make a clear comment. I was also strongly focused, or maybe fixated, on my faith. It was somewhat understandable since I was housed during the Easter season. I relied on my spiritual beliefs for survival. These thoughts were readily accessible in my memory bank and provided me both comfort and direction.

It is convenient to draw from that which you know, and my faith is important to me. I also had grandiose thoughts, which is quite common with this illness. There was a heightened recognition of my faith and an overall hope for a better world.

It was actually painful reading the journals, knowing that they were the very best I could do with the daily assignments. At some point it was exhausting trying to generate my thoughts. Usually the words came easily, but at other times I had to force my ideas. My doodles probably came at those points. There was no right or wrong, as I mentioned at the beginning of this chapter, but the journals forced me to step out and formulate thoughts without feeling pressured. I did the best that I could. I had to surrender to the doctors, the hospital, the drugs, and ultimately, to the illness. These journals allowed me to chronicle my journey in a simple, insightful way.

10

A NEW NAME

I now have a new name for the existing illness: *bipolar disorder I, manic phase*. This diagnosis, according to the Diagnostic and Statistical Manual Disorders, involves "episodes of severe mania and often depression."

My doctor gave me this tag, which more accurately explains my condition. But oh, how I hate tags, diagnoses, and suppositions! Bipolar illness involves periods of severe mood episodes, from mania to depression. Often patients experience heightened euphoria and happiness, followed by drastic depression and guilt. The disease can also cause the person to lose touch with reality. There is less need for sleep, a marked increase in energy, and an increased sexual desire. During a manic episode, individuals may engage in risky or reckless behavior. For example, someone may indulge in risky sexual behavior, spend excessive amounts of money, or make impulsive decisions. The only reckless behavior I can remember is buying a cartload of Easter toys at Walmart.

I keep coming back to the same question: "What causes bipolar illness?"

According to WebMD, with a medical review by Smitha Bhandari on March 8, 2021:

> Doctors don't completely understand the causes of bipolar
> disorder. But they've gained a great understanding in recent

years of the bipolar spectrum, which includes the elated highs of mania to the lows of major depression, along with various mood states between these two extremes. Bipolar disorder seems to often run in families and there appears to be a genetic part to this mood disorder. There is also growing evidence that environment and lifestyle issues have an effect on the disorder's severity. Stressful life events—or alcohol or drug abuse—can make bipolar disorder more difficult to treat. Experts believe bipolar disorder is partly caused by an underlying problem with specific brain circuits and the functioning of brain chemicals called neurotransmitters.

Three brain chemicals—norepinephrine (noradrenaline), serotonin, and dopamine—are involved in both brain and bodily functions. Norepinephrine and serotonin have been consistently linked to psychiatric mood disorders such as depression and bipolar disorder. Nerve pathways within areas of the brain that regulate pleasure and emotional reward are regulated by dopamine. Disruption of circuits that communicate using dopamine in other brain areas appears connected to psychosis and schizophrenia, a severe mental disorder characterized by distortions in reality and illogical thought patterns and behaviors.

The brain chemical serotonin is connected to many body functions such as sleep, wakefulness, eating, sexual activity, impulsivity, learning, and memory. Researchers believe that abnormal functioning of brain circuits that involve serotonin as a chemical messenger contributes to mood disorders (depression and bipolar disorder).

My bipolar illness almost always presents itself as mania—with high energy, sleeplessness, and racing thoughts. I have difficulty focusing, and my speech is erratic. I have grandiose thoughts coupled with ideas of spirituality. My ideas are extraordinary, or so I think. Severe mania is infinitely easier to detect than depression. "Bouncing off the walls" is a good indicator.

My talking is endless. I can't wait to share my ideas and thoughts, and it's difficult to wait my turn. A bipolar episode is fairly easy to identify, especially when you know the person. A little later our family developed a cueing system: a small tap from a family member was an indicator that I was speaking in excess.

Writing this book has always been a bone of contention for my family. To them it is a trigger of mania. Why would she write a book? What would she have to say? Everyone is on guard for another manic episode. There is always some truth to what I do; it's just exaggerated, maybe unattainable when I am manic. Oddly, there is an excitement when I am manic. My writing and creativity are heightened, and I relish the high. But it's a fine line . . .

On January 20, 2002, I wrote in my journal:

> I continue to "speedball," as I call it. I AM NOT GOING TO THE HOSPITAL! This disease is a curse and I am fighting so hard. With this "speedballing," my mind is racing too fast. Too many thoughts are coming in. Will it all stop? I can definitely multi-task and everything will be perfect. No problems . . .

One example is an afternoon when I drove to Cayucos and befriended a homeless man. I bought him coffee, and we visited in the restaurant by the pier for a long time. We talked politics, families, and life in general. When I shared about my afternoon, my family went ballistic. I justified that we were in a public place. A sense of invincibility is also common for me. The world is so interesting that I need to experience it all. Fear does not enter into my picture.

On the other hand, my depressive episodes may include low energy, little motivation, and loss of interest in daily activities. For the most part, I experience very little depression. In a journal tucked away, I discovered a couple of dark thoughts I wrote of suicide. To be sure, I have never attempted suicide, but it has crossed my mind. One time I contemplated drowning in the oceans of Hawaii. Perhaps everyone would think it was just a fluke accident. The other time I envisioned driving off a highway bridge, one that I drive on a daily basis. Who would really miss me? I could spare everyone a lot of problems.

Another journal entry regarding my depression:

At one point I knew that the depression had begun, but it hasn't set in too bad. My doctor and I tried to curb my wonderings by installing new, bright bulbs in the closet. The therapist said I should practice a routine for bed between 8 p.m. to 8 a.m. Sounds simple, we'll see how it works. My longing for normalcy doesn't last too long. The thoughts are hurtful and I would prefer to crawl down a hole and disappear.

In 2002, I wrote:
This sadness is horrendous. It's hard to smile: it's hard to be positive. When everyone else is having a great time, I can't figure it out. Why can't I have the fun I used to have? Why do I find myself faking it, forcing myself to fit in? Basically, I am a fraud and I'm afraid someone will stop and notice my obvious unhappiness, my blatant misery. But no one seems to notice.

Hopelessness accompanies this sadness. Sure, the sadness is bad enough, but when coupled with a lack of hope, there is a real fear that the depression will never end.

Another entry read:

The parties are not fun. The family gatherings are work. I crave for alone time because I don't want to be with anyone else. To tell you the truth, pangs of misery, of anti-social behavior have enveloped me. So, I hide. I hide in my shell, like a turtle, a sea crab, a chameleon. I blend in with the crowd, a disappearance from the world around me. Maybe I could suck into my body so deeply that I no longer exist.

Getting out of bed is a chore. I check the clock and hope for 8 p.m. so I can crawl back in again. Chores must be done, but I'd rather not do them. And then comes the feelings of inadequacy. No longer am I attractive, intelligent, interesting. I am unworthy to be loved and certainly unworthy to deserve praise.

With this disorder, treatment can help, but the condition cannot be cured. It is chronic and can last for years or a lifetime.

According to WebMD:

- There are more than three million cases in the US per year.
- As many as 20 percent of people complaining of depression to their doctor actually have bipolar disorder.
- About half of people with bipolar disorder have seen three professionals before being diagnosed correctly.

- It takes an average of ten years for people to enter treatment after symptoms begin. This is caused in part by delays in diagnosis.
- Most people with bipolar disorder have additional psychiatric conditions, such as substance abuse or anxiety. That can make overall diagnoses more challenging.

In a way, I was comforted knowing that my illness had a name. But I felt pigeonholed, like a woman with a scarlet letter. I wondered whether there were any opportunities for improvement. My mind couldn't quite grasp the severity of it all—for someone like me who tried to live life right. No drugs, no criminal record, nothing. It didn't make any sense. And then, when the doctor told me it was most likely a lifelong illness, with no cure, I could barely fathom the gravity of it all. She said that treatment can help, but management is the only key. Prescription medication is basically a requirement.

What would people think when they discovered the truth? How would it change the things I loved to do? Would this revelation hurt my family, my friends, the children I worked with? Would my life drastically change because of my diagnosis? Too many questions, not enough answers.

One part of my treatment success was my aftercare. I was admitted to the French Partial Hospitalization program on April 3, 1997, and completed the outpatient program on May 5, 1997. At that point, I felt well enough to return to my grand jury appointment.

It was the purpose of the plan to prepare you for reentry into society and your family unit. We focused on objectives, including program goals within the unit and goals outside of the program. The targets were very specific and were always discussed with an assigned counselor. My doctor kept track of my progress and met with me daily. I attended classes four days a week, from 10 a.m. to 3 p.m. A passenger van shuttled me from home to San Luis Obispo since we needed to be mindful of the assimilation of the drugs in my brain.

My activities included listing fifty things for which I was grateful. I was also to read appropriate books, such as *An Unquiet Mind* by Kay Redfield Jamison. I also designed objects with clay and listened to uplifting music. This last item would assist me during bouts of sleeplessness.

My program plan stated:

> Cindy will talk about her bipolar disorder in at least one group per day and elicit feedback from others in the group. She will also cooperate with the prescribed medication regime and will participate in the monitoring of its effects.

The medications played a huge role in healing my illness—it took so much time. However, I was amazed at how quickly the brain heals itself in tandem with treatment by trained professionals.

Perhaps the most important part of the class was the developing of my Personal Relapse Prevention Plan. My plan was comprised of three triggers: sleeplessness, physical health, and incorrect prioritizing. My counselor and I worked on this final note card together, and it was a tool of reference. There was even a list of activities to prevent a relapse (e.g., gardening, reading, scrapbooking, and listening to calm, soothing music). This plan's purpose was to have a tool at hand and a means of execution when an episode began to present itself.

The program was a godsend to me as I have always been a good student. Since the subject was about me, I had to excel. The trip in the van was calming and allowed me to observe without pressure. I liked many of the daily activities—the crafts and the questionnaires about moods. You could interact with other patients or keep to yourself. We were instructed on how to maintain personal space within ourselves and for others. All of us were healing at different rates.

I knew from past experience that I would have to struggle, fight, and claw my way back to life. I had my doctor, my medications, and my plan of action. Hopefully, the world would take me into its arms and nurse me back to life.

11

THE BIG "C"

The nursing back to life took only a short time—maybe a few months at the outset. I was then on to my next adventure in my interesting journey. Things were on the upswing. We sold our business, so I had more time to explore.

To be honest, I had been neglecting my general health and decided it was the right opportunity to join a gym. Even though I was past my prime (at forty), I decided to give it a go. It was actually daunting walking through the doors of the gym. Truth be told, I had done some exploration prior to this entry—a few drive-bys, so to speak. This visit was a pledge of sorts, an actual commitment.

The "workout" girls at the gym donned cutaway midriff tops with Lycra leggings that were designed to enhance every possible curve. Even the guys showed off their biceps with cutaway tank tops. The mirrored walls reflected their bulging muscles. I gulped and nearly ran for the door, but my inner promise forced me to stay and give it a try.

Since I had no clue what to do, I hired a regimented bodybuilder as my personal trainer. She made a commitment to me. In fact, we made a pact of sorts—I'd pay the money, and she would whip me into shape. Nothing too drastic, not too many muscles. Nothing that would cause me to wear those silly midriffs!

One day, through self-assessment, I discovered a new "muscle" that I thought should be checked. It was in the upper outer quadrant of my right breast. Remembering the rantings of my OB-GYN, I thought it might be a good move on my part to call his office. He performed a fine-needle biopsy in the office and aspirated a small amount of blood. Since this test was inconclusive, he sent me for a mammogram, which was negative. The ultrasound did not reveal a mass in the upper outer quadrant, but did show a solid lesion in the upper inner quadrant. A core needle biopsy guided by an ultrasound machine presented a positive reading. The biopsy felt like an ear-piercing device, just a quick pinch. The core sample resembled small spaghetti noodles. They were 0.5 to 2.10 centimeters in length, and I vividly remember studying the samples.

With this core sample, there were not any more questions: it was infiltrating ductal adenocarcinoma. It was poorly differentiated, without evidence of vascular invasion or necrosis. I got "the call," an SOS of sorts, from the radiologist's office while I was at the gym. Could I come to his office that morning? I knew. Whenever a doctor wants to see you ASAP, there is trouble to be delivered—in person, of course.

No one was available to go with me other than my tenderheart-ed father. I had hoped he could drive me home in case the news was worse than I anticipated. So wrong! Dad began crying as we entered the doctor's office. Useless, he was useless, and I needed to focus. The doctor began explaining my diagnosis, and I tried to hang on to his every word, waiting to ask all the necessary questions. The radiolo-gist felt we should act quickly since he suspected that the cancer was fast-growing.

Sweet dad and Cindy, 2000

The next couple of weeks were a blur. I needed a surgeon, a radiologist, and an oncologist. Fortunately, I already had a remarkable OB-GYN. I had no contacts, so we got busy, and the favored doctors in the area began to surface.

We received some guidance from my sister-in-law, a nuclear pharmacist. She suggested that we research a procedure called sentinel node biopsy. The biopsy is done directly before surgery and involves a radioactive tracer drug (a dye), which travels directly from the tumor to the sentinel lymph node. This diagnostic procedure provides the surgeon with information regarding the spread of the cancer. The nodes are presented in order, and if the sentinel node (the first node) is clear, most likely the remaining nodes are clear as well. The dye's pattern determines the spread of the cancer. Locating the sentinel node is the key. This procedure appeared logical to me, even though it was still considered experimental.

It turned out that the surgeon I wanted did not perform the procedure, so I would have to look elsewhere. Enter Dr. Michelle

Strasen, one of two doctors in the county who were currently performing the procedure. She was a no-nonsense country gal. In our initial consultation, we discussed the approach to my dilemma. Did I want a lumpectomy, a mastectomy, radiation, or chemotherapy? So much to digest! She drew a simple chart on a notepaper, listing the procedures and the rates of survival. Yes, rates of survival. These numbers would determine how my life would play out.

I was forty-four years old, with a lot of life to live, and a family I adored. In some ways, my choice was easy. I chose the most aggressive course of action, with the highest rate of survival, and I never looked back. My treatment would include a lumpectomy, radiation, and chemotherapy. I hoped God would give me the courage to survive the coming challenges with a degree of dignity.

So two weeks later, I began my journey. The sentinel node was removed, followed by an additional seven nodes, to reduce any possibility of the spread of the cancer. My doctor was correct when she told me that the surgery would be the easiest part of my treatment—only the beginning of a tough battle. How right she was!

The doctors conferred and determined that, since I was young and healthy, my radiation and chemotherapy could be administered concurrently. Radiation was scheduled five times a week for six weeks, and chemotherapy would be administered every three weeks for six months. With that schedule, I had a new job.

My radiologist was a personable doctor but had many patients, and so appointments were scheduled back-to-back. If you were late, you were considered a no-show, and your slot was promptly given away. Most patients, perhaps *all* patients, counted down the number of remaining treatments, so it was vital to be on time and be ready. It was a hassle to have daily appointments, but the weekends were free. Great measures were taken to pinpoint the area of the tumor because the radiation needed to be exact and reach any potential cancer surrounding the site of the tumor. In order to mark the area, they tattooed my skin, which made it easier to treat.

I had great faith in my oncologist from the get-go. Cancer treatment varies from patient to patient, depending on the need, and he customized my "poison cocktail" based on my treatment plan. He provided me with his personal phone number in case I needed him. It was common knowledge that he was a great advocate for all patients, even the uninsured.

My first treatment was memorable. It was in a large room with recliners along the walls. Each patient had infusion bags hanging from a movable pole. Two patients shared a nurse who monitored their infusion and their care. These nurses were angels—empathetic and efficient. I didn't understand why some people chose not to chat. The meaning of "conservation of energy" was explained to me. One only uses the minimum amount of energy that one has to spare. You need to draw energy for the remainder of the day from what energy you have left. This caused people to appear like zombies, simply existing for the treatment. So a lot of my treatment time was alone time. I only had books and small projects to pass the hours.

This chemotherapy and the regimen were based on a cycle that was determined by the hours, the week, the month. The side effects of the infusions were brutal. The first day was clear sailing, but the second day found me in bed with intense retching. Basically, I was confined to the house. My weight would fluctuate, sometimes eight or ten pounds from week to week. The retching was usually triggered by smells, almost like morning sickness when pregnant. I remember a time when the kids prepared dinner, fajitas, and were so excited to share them with me. I took one smell and couldn't stay in the kitchen. The fried food smelled putrid. I'm sure the kids didn't understand my reaction. Another time Karl and I went to dinner with some friends, and I couldn't eat the entrée that I had selected. It was all so confusing, so unexpected. Comfort foods like macaroni and cheese or pudding were my primary choices.

I had another ally in my treatment process, an unlikely one. It was my brown-haired chihuahua, Jody. She became my adopted companion when my daughter went off to college. Jody would burrow her body next to me. She had a sixth sense that I needed her, and oh, she was so intuitive. When visitors couldn't visit, Jody was always at my side.

Cindy with her faithful companion, Jody, 1999

Before you could actually receive an infusion, your blood would be tested. The test results would determine the levels of your white blood count. If it was too low, you could not receive the infusion. Subsequently, an injection of Neupogen would be administered, and you would be sent home. Not only would you be devastated that you couldn't receive the treatment, but the side effects were brutal in a different way. The medication would settle in your large bones—the hips, the thighs—and would cause great pain. After one injection, I decided to try to find some relief in our whirlpool tub. I got into the tub but couldn't get out. Luckily, my dad stopped by the house and wrestled me out of the tub. Back to the bed I limped.

At one point, my blood counts were so low that I was confined to my home, could only eat prepackaged foods, and could receive no visitors. I couldn't go outside of the house because even a step on a small pebble might impair my immune system. Infections were to be avoided at all costs.

Other patients had even worse scenarios. My heart would ache when parents brought their kids in for treatment. The nurse angels always had extra time for the kids. The parents hauled in televisions and toys to keep their kids happy and busy, but the sadness in the parents' eyes was nearly unbearable.

Another situation that touched me was the plight of a young couple. They were in a quandary because chemotherapy almost always caused infertility. His medical insurance did not cover sperm conservation, and they couldn't afford the procedure. *Somehow my cancer didn't seem so significant.*

Due to the fact that I have very small veins, we had to take another approach to the regular needle insertion. In an outpatient procedure, the doctor inserted a quarter-sized port under the skin. This port enabled the nurses to inject my drugs directly into the carotid artery. Weekly blood draws were drawn from the port, as well. This quarter-sized object prevented constant pokes, which was a real blessing and the right choice.

There were many side effects that I did *not* experience, such as lymphedema, total exhaustion, and loss of muscle mass. On the other hand, I was immediately thrown into menopause (I was premenopausal at the onset of the cancer). I also had some hair loss and was plagued with "chemo brain."

According to the American Cancer Society, chemo brain is a decrease in mental sharpness and the inability to remember certain things. You have trouble finishing tasks, concentrating, and learning new skills. Even though its exact cause isn't known, it can happen anytime you have cancer treatments. When I couldn't balance an uncomplicated bank statement, I knew I was in trouble. And spelling . . . I have always been an exceptional speller, but now I often couldn't formulate the words. Incorrect or out-of-sequence words would come out of my mouth, and I was confused by what I was saying. In my mind, I knew the words were wrong, but I couldn't control them. They were already spoken. So strange.

But as quickly as the chemo brain arrived, it improved after my last treatment. It took about three months to completely vanish. I wish I had known about this syndrome earlier so I could have known I wasn't crazy.

After this six-month fiasco, normal life resumed, and my strength and stamina began to return. Here was another life experience added to my arsenal.

12

THE GOOD FIGHT

I was fortunate: I had a wonderful husband and three great kids. There were issues though. Cancer was hard on everyone. None of us knew what to expect, what to do. Perhaps it would have been helpful to have had family counseling, something, anything. But we didn't; we just muddled through it all.

At about this time a music video performed by Reba McEntire was shown on television. Its name was "What Do You Say?" It showed the parents raising their teenagers through many scenarios, with hard choices to be made (e.g., adult bookstores, underage drinking, and finally, the death of their mother from cancer). According to the video:

Her every breath is weaker than the last. And lately when she sleeps, she talks about the past. Her husband knows she's tired of holdin' on. She looks at him and says she wants to go home. What do you say in a moment like this, when you can't find the words to tell it like it is? Just close your eyes and let your heart lead the way. Ooh, what do you say?

When the video would play, we would all sob, especially the girls. What was going to happen to Mom? What was going to happen to our little family unit? This "thing" was happening, and we had no control over it. Why? Why?

One day our daughter came home from school upset. She explained how everyone always asked how *I* was and no one cared about how *she* was. All members of the family, especially the kids, needed to be okay, or at least somewhat okay. We had been so engrossed in just slaying the dragon that we hadn't paid too much attention to the kids. If we wanted to win this battle, we would have to play as a team. It was important that we constantly assessed how the kids were handling the mess.

The girls played high school basketball, and we had always been their biggest supporters. Their coach played a pivotal role in their development and was an outstanding mentor to them. His consistency provided them with the normalcy they needed at the time. I joked to my doctors that I was going to wear a paper bag over my head so that I could attend every game. No germ would stop me!

But somehow, someway, we made it through the "Big C." My doctor has watched me closely over the years. Following my chemotherapy and radiation, I was prescribed Tamoxifen for five years and then Raloxifene indefinitely. If another drug appears on the market that my doctor feels is appropriate for me, I am open to yet another drug. The medical field continues to evolve, and I hope to be on the cutting edge of treatment options.

Tamoxifen is a type of hormone therapy that attaches to hormone receptors in breast cancer cells. Once the medication is inside the cells, it stops the cancer from accessing the hormones they need to multiply and grow. Other preventative measures that the doctor implemented for me included the following:

- Annual mammogram.
- Annual ovarian cancer screening—transvaginal ultrasound with Doppler flow.
- Added CA-125 to blood screening for high-risk patients. It is a simple test that measures the amount of protein CA-125 in your blood, and it may be used to look at early signs of ovarian cancer.
- Annual magnetic resonance imaging (MRI).
- And always, self-breast exam.

It would be remiss of me not to take the opportunity to share with you the signs and symptoms of breast cancer. According to Cancer Health:

- Discovery of a lump or thickened area of the breast tissue. The lump is usually hard, painless and has uneven edges
- Change in breast size or shape.
- Swelling of the whole breast.
- Breast or nipple pain.
- A change in appearance of your breast such as becoming flaky, thickened, and red.
- Nipple discharge (other than breast milk).

This journey has enabled me to have faith—faith in my family, faith in my doctors, and faith in myself. Faith that such a difficult voyage is manageable. With most journeys come unexpected adversities. My thoughts now drift to other questions. Will I pass this breast cancer gene to my daughters, my granddaughters?

A rather simple blood test can now determine your ability to pass on your genes: it's called BRAC. The test can track the mutations in my DNA that increase the risk of the breast cancer gene. The test is offered to those who are likely to have inherited the mutation based on personal or family history of ovarian cancer. My doctor encouraged me to take the test. Not knowing what the results would show, I reluctantly followed his advice. To my relief, and my daughters' relief, it was determined that I do *not* carry the gene. This test is rarely covered by medical insurance and is expensive. It's an avenue you may want to explore.

In a publication of the Susan G. Komen Breast Cancer Foundation, Gloria, a four-year survivor, writes:

> The struggles a woman faces while recovering from cancer can be difficult. She has to find the ideal balance between moving beyond her breast cancer experience and focusing too much on the possibility of recurrence. Being aware of the increased risks of recurrence is important, but so is living a full healthy life. The concern never goes away, but it is important to fill your life with other good things like giving and sharing with others. In doing so, you find that weeks go by without you focusing on what may happen in the future. Being involved in volunteer opportunities is a great way to give back to others and at the same time it strengthens you.

I volunteered at the American Cancer Society's Road to Recovery program. It is a program that provides free transportation for cancer patients to their treatment appointments. This was just a small way to give back to patients as they walk their journey. Because I had been in their circumstances, it was easy to relate to their struggles. Sometimes they wanted to talk; often they did not. Whatever they needed, I tried to provide.

To my surprise, I have been proactive about my breast cancer. One would think that I would be private, hesitant to share with others. In my own quiet way, I have been on a crusade about self-breast examinations and mammograms. I even appeared on a local news station regarding a new machine that a hospital had acquired. It's never a bother to ask your doctor for a quick check. *You* are your best and truest ally. To wait an entire year until your next mammogram could be too long. Always err on the side of caution.

In comparison to postpartum depression and bipolar illness, cancer was easier to share with others—the diagnosis, the treatment, the aftercare. To me, there was little shame in having breast cancer. Through no fault of my own, it simply appeared. A protocol was in place to solve, or attempt to solve, the problem. If not this, then that. Mental illness is much more elusive. There is not *one* protocol, not *one* plan of action. Providing treatment is challenging and usually takes a great deal of time.

We fought the good fight with breast cancer and won!

13

MAINLY MEDS

Unlike the standard protocol for the treatment of breast cancer, treatment for a mental illness is much more complex. It's a process of hit and miss, trial and error, with no definitive outcome. What may work this month may not be the answer the next month. For the doctor, there is but an educated hope that a plan of action can be formulated and implemented.

For the most part, there are two prongs of treatment: psychotherapy and drug management. Although psychiatric medications don't *cure* mental illness, they can greatly improve the situation and its symptoms. As the years pass, there is a greater variety of drugs from which to choose.

It is commonplace to utilize a combination of drugs—kind of a cocktail. Sometimes just one drug doesn't solve the problem, so a plan is devised to promote a different outcome. Instead of using a single drug, a combination (often in small dosages) can be most effective. The psychiatrist is trained in this type of drug configuration. Some drugs are originally designed to manage one type of symptom but can be utilized to aid another medical condition. For instance, one drug, Lamictal, was formulated to assist patients with epileptic seizures. For me, it was used to quiet the rapid-fire neurons in my brain.

I have been on a myriad of drugs, and it has been mentally difficult for me to count out the medications prescribed and swallow them on a daily basis. Previously my only drug of choice was ibuprofen or aspirin. Now my prescriptions always remind me of my illness. I am slow to add even vitamins to my handful because I don't want to be reminded of it all.

In the book *An Unquiet Mind* by Kay Redfield Jamison, she states:

> . . . the war I waged against myself is not an uncommon one. The major clinical problem in treating manic depressive illness is not that there are not effective medications—there are—but that patients refuse to take them.

Refusal has never been an issue for me. I remain drug compliant and defer to my physicians for my drug regimen. Dr. Speed was always open to my concerns and questions. During each session she had me recite, from memory, my current medication list and encouraged me to revise my reference card, which I kept in my wallet in case of an emergency. This small procedure kept me focused on myself and my current drugs.

In October 2003, Dr. Speed became frustrated regarding my treatment and its effects on me. She sought the advice of Dr. Robert Gerner, a psychiatrist with a subspecialty in psychopharmacology. She hoped that he would provide a much-needed course of action for me. She was concerned that we had not been able to stop the mania from recurring. Perhaps he would have some suggestions about my mood stabilizer/antidepressant combination. After a brief summary of my personal history, she then described my treatment. The time frames are as follows:

- Approximately 1980: Mrs. Wittstrom had her first episode of depression following the birth of her first child, approximately twenty-three years ago. She required hospitalization and was treated with lithium and antipsychotics, which caused a dysphoric reaction. She was weaned off the medications and did well for eighteen years.
- 1997: The second episode occurred in early 1997, and appears to have been a mixed state. The combination of Depakote, Klonopin, and Risperdal stabilized her mood. Ambien has been in use for sleep since that time. By August 1997, her hair was falling out and she complained of cognitive slowing, both of which resolved when we stopped the Depakote. I hoped that she would do well going off mood stabilizers since she had gone so long between the first and second episodes.
- 1998: In mid-1998, we started Lamictal because of waxing and waning of depression and irritability. Her mood stabilized, but in December 1998 she had a full-blown manic episode. I do not believe there has been a problem with medication compliance, and at the time she was taking Lamictal. The addition of Zyprexa worked well to stop the mania, but, of course, caused a lot of weight gain. She tapered off Zyprexa and continued on Lamictal and Ambien.
- 1999: This was the year of medical problems. She developed gallstones, but handled the surgery well. She was diagnosed with breast cancer and got through chemotherapy and radiation no worse than anyone does mood-wise.

- 2000: We increased Lamictal in February because of depression, which worsened after the completion of her radiation therapy. When the depression worsened, we tried Zoloft, and eventually Effexor, which was successful in lifting her back to "neutral" for most of the next year.
- 2001: Patient became manic again. Lamictal plus Zyprexa and Neurontin got things stabilized. We switched Zyprexa to Geodon to avoid the weight gain. Gradually, as she cycled down, we decreased the Neurontin and stopped Geodon. She has a good sense of when to use Geodon if she feels she's hyper or irritable. She did well on Lamictal, Neurontin, and Ambien.
- By April 2002, patient was depressed again. We had to add Effexor—it worked well again, and I have been reluctant to take her off it since that time.
- Everything went well until June 2003, when she cycled into mania again. She was taking Lamictal, Neurontin, Effexor. To control the mania, we added Geodon and Neurontin. Ambien continues to help with sleep.

Dr. Speed concluded her letter with:

I have several questions. Clearly, Mrs. Wittstrom's cycle length is shortened. I am concerned that the use of Effexor, while helpful, may be adding to the frequency of her mood cycles. In addition, the Lamictal-Neurontin combination doesn't prevent manic episodes well enough. Can you make suggestions about where to go next with her medications?

CINDY C. WITTSTROM . 87

After our appointment, Dr. Gerner summarized that he concurred that I was having relatively rapid mood swings.

> Mrs. Wittstrom appears to have a sensitive biological vulnerability to manias. I do remark that her first episode, in 1979, was clearly biochemically precipitated (with the birth of her first child). The second episode in 1997 occurred after a circadian lengthening (flying from Italy to California). She is aware that lack of sleep reliably precipitates manic episodes. Her sleep is generally poor because of hot flashes/sweating due to chemotherapy-induced menopause.

His observation and recommendations were as follows:

- Her BPI disorder is exacerbated by her anti-estrogen treatment.
- I'm not sure she can recognize her hypomania.
- Since she is always on the edge of a switch, I would aggressively continue to treat any insomnia. Ideally, she should not fly through more than one time zone at a time. Use melatonin when flying.
- Discontinue Effexor, taper off slowly
- Might be a good candidate for thyroid augmentation to reduce cycling.
- Add lithium.
- Suggest other options for cycling.

- Advise full spectrum of incandescent lights by bedside. This can help her cycle.
- If she cycles into a depression, I would be inclined to add Wellbutrin.
- Continue her other meds as-is.

As I mentioned previously, Dr. Gerner is a psychopharmacologist. He had additional schooling beyond that of a psychiatrist. He has a keen understanding of drug-to-drug interactions, the half-life of specific drugs (how long the medication stays in the body), protein binding (how available the medication is to the body), and polymorphic genes (genes that vary widely from person to person).

It took the competence and willingness of both doctors to make an accurate assessment of my illness. The fact that Dr. Speed reached out to another outstanding physician speaks volumes about *her* ability to collaborate. I'm glad that she's on my team.

14

A MISSED DREAM

Choices are different when you have a debilitating illness, especially one that cannot be seen. My illness can only be apparent when it is beyond my control and it becomes crippling for myself and for my family. It comes and goes at will. One fact is true: it lies in wait and will eventually surface.

Going back maybe five years or so, our parent church began the process of closing our quaint little church in Shandon, which was located across from the community park. Shandon has a population of approximately 1,200 residents, 75 percent of which are Hispanic and are associated with the grape industry. This hamlet is surrounded by large farms and ranches, and there are only two small markets and no other services. The closest town is about twenty minutes away. Shandon relies on services from this neighboring town, and it is governed by the County of San Luis Obispo.

We have roots in this community. Karl and his family moved to the area to farm in 1960. His mom was a dynamic lady who was capable of doing anything she wanted—from milking cows to teaching educable handicapped kids. She played the organ at the little church and taught English as a second language to the residents of the community, as well. Karl's dad was in the Lions' Club and was always bringing forward needed projects. He was usually successful in securing county funds for the community.

Needless to say, it was a good fit for us to join this small congregation. When Karl's mom became increasingly ill with cancer, we spent more time at our adopted church. All told, we spent about twelve years there and cherished our many friendships as our faith deepened.

I was particularly touched by the kids. They ran to the church for any and all events, and usually they came without their parents, just with their siblings or their cousins. The church was a safety net: somewhere to feel at home, somewhere to get a bite to eat, somewhere to learn about the one who we call God.

Kids like crafts, and boy, did we have them! We had every known feather and bead, all colors of paints and paper, and always *lots* of glue and tape. Art projects lined the windows—we wanted to show off their accomplishments. Miss Gay taught them music (not available in their daily school life). The schedule was fluid; we always made time for the important concerns of the day. We encouraged the kids to demonstrate Christ's love for all.

We organized kids' club and youth group after school on Wednesdays and, of course, Sunday school. In the summer we held Vacation Bible School with about sixty kids in attendance for a week. It was always our intention for any children's activities to be free of charge.

It took a while to establish ourselves in the community. Many of the Hispanic families were interrelated and were wary of strangers. When one family would agree to send their kids to church, we'd usually get another family's kids not long after. It was fun because we were actually teaching another generation of children.

So as I began to say . . . the parent church decided to close our small church because we didn't generate "enough" funds and didn't recruit "enough" members. Of course, they didn't count the little ones, or the numbers would have shown them a totally different trend!

This church was surely much more than a building; it was a family. The kids didn't understand why we stopped meeting after school. They could no longer pick a silly pumpkin from the Santa Margarita Ranch, slurp root beer floats on the front step, hold the keys down on the autoharp, or do messy art projects. They just knew that their Wednesdays weren't the same.

Don't get me wrong; it wasn't always easy. We had to invent new projects, interesting games, and fun snacks. There were a few discipline problems. But the benefits greatly outweighed the work. Even my dad would join us on Wednesdays. The kids would call him Popo and made sure he had water and snacks. *They* learned many life lessons, too.

As the Wednesdays came to a halt, Miss Gay and I made certain that each child walked home with a new Bible, a gift from their "old" church. It was the least we could do since there wouldn't be any more kids' club activities.

In the meantime, our son, Chad, purchased Karl's parents' place from the estate. This strengthened our ties to Shandon, as well. The time finally came, and the small church's charter was closed and we were evicted. The church was scheduled to be sold—lock, stock, and barrel. The parent church had the notion that they could sell the property for a hefty profit and that it would happen quickly. Suffice it to say, the church building began to go into disrepair and fell in and out of escrow.

Well, my granddaughter, Grace, and I drove to the Shandon Market, and I noticed the "For Sale" sign hanging half-tilted on the fence. It stopped me in my tracks. I guess I had assumed that it had already sold. I pulled the car into the ditch and had her write down all the particulars. I took it from there.

Possible plans began to gather in my brain. The property actually presented itself to some very real possibilities: church services (of course), computer classes, after-school programs, Spanish/English classes, tutoring, yoga, Boy/Girl Scouts, personal finance classes (Chad could teach). The ideas were endless. I envisioned a Shandon Community Center, something the little town desperately needed. It would be the community's project, and I could create a nonprofit to operate it. Money for the property purchase would not be an issue since my parents had left me an inheritance. Our current pastor indicated an interest in using "junior" pastors for the ministerial duties.

In my mind, everything was falling into place. I even put the property into escrow twice. The parent church wanted to be rid of the church, so they were quite willing to lower the price. My excitement continued to build. But this excitement was my downfall. Remember, my excitement can often be viewed as my mania. It's like the chicken or the egg, what comes first?

Whatever the order, my dreams, my opportunities become squelched. And that is exactly what happened! That "fire in my belly" had to be extinguished, not by myself, but by others. No one was willing to carry the torch with me or cheer me on. One family member came out and said he wouldn't help and not to count on him. My ideas fell on deaf ears. Ultimately, I let my second offer fall out of escrow.

I'm not sure when the disappointment and anger began to stew, but stew they did. I experienced a real "kick in the gut" and began to question my logic.

Why couldn't people like me have dreams? Are we doomed to failure? Is it foolhardy to imagine a dream? Maybe my dreams are not worthy of attention. Maybe I am incapable of executing my ideas.

At this point, I felt as though I was being punished, and I had done nothing wrong.

If the truth be told, today I would handle the situation entirely differently. To placate the family, I would simply purchase the property, repair it, and let it sit for a while. When they witnessed my problem-solving and plan of execution, I would proceed slowly, recruit a team of volunteers, and accomplish my goals in a timely fashion. Spontaneous actions should not be equated with mania!

What a limiting illness! This was a missed opportunity, not of my choosing.

15

A VACATION IN SANTA BARBARA

Anyone who knows me is aware that my bags are always packed; from a shampoo bottle to a clock, an umbrella, and even earplugs, I can be ready to go in a moment's notice. I'll travel anywhere. My vaccinations are in current order, and my passport is updated. Some of our best trips have included a bicycle trip to Belgium, a business trip to China, a cruise down the Adriatic coast, a trek up to Machu Pichu, and most recently, a photo safari to Africa. I always attribute my curiosity to that of a small-town girl wanting to see the world outside my own little bubble.

An uninvited guest in our camp in Zimbabwe, 2022

But my vacation to Santa Barbara was a different kind of trip, one that I need to explain. My journey began similarly to my former hospitalizations: with lack of sleep, coupled with bipolar mania. Our decision to pursue this placement was a bit premature—or so I was told by my doctor, Dr. Margaret Bauman. She felt that because July 4, 2019, was an upcoming holiday, I would be better served if I was admitted a day or two earlier. Santa Barbara was my closest option since French Hospital had closed long ago.

There was another factor that precipitated my intake, specifically my sleeping medication. The current practice is that a pharmacy will only dispense thirty days of a psychotropic medication at a given time. For a chronic insomniac, this presents a very real dilemma. Even one or two nights without sleep can catapult me into a semi-manic phase, and so I take any and all steps to avoid a disruption in medicating myself.

In our many travels to Mexico, I generally purchase a sleep medication, usually Ambien, along with any other needed antibiotics or bacterial creams. Never has there been an issue. There are pharmacies galore, two or three on each street, regardless of the town or city. It is commonplace for U.S. residents to purchase these medications without a doctor's prescription, at a much-discounted price. It is big business!

Therein lies the problem. The old adage, "If it appears too good to be true . . ." In my research, this problem is widespread. One article explained that a mother would travel to Mexico to purchase insulin for her son because it was so much cheaper; and she was taking a risk because the medications are not regulated. My problem, we believed, was due to the packaging. These drugs are usually compiled in foreign countries—for instance, India—and the pills are irregular in their formatting. A bottle or bubble pack may indicate the correct number of milligrams, but the individual pill dosage is irregular. One night the pill might contain three milligrams, and the next night the "identical" pill might be fifteen milligrams. All of the pills *look* the same—that's the deception. In 2017, the World Health Organization estimated that 10 percent of drugs in developing countries were either substandard or falsified.

My psychiatrist, Dr. Margaret Bauman, surmised that I fell into the "packaging" scenario, which disrupted my sleep cycle and sent me spinning to Santa Barbara. Prior to my admission, we (Karl and I) were in close contact via email and messaging with the doctor. What an immediate response time, compared with the old telephone, "Leave a message" days!

Upon entry to Cottage Hospital, I was handed off to a competent in-house psychiatrist. I put my trust in yet another professional with the hopes that she could get my episode under control. My initial room was solitary, directly across from the nurses' station. For two days I was unaware that there were lights under my bed, making it easier for the nurses to make the fifteen-minute checks for my safety. I would often stumble over to the night nurses' station and want to chat. They would gently usher me back to my room. I knew I needed to be sleeping, but my mind continued to race. As I began to stabilize, my wanderings subsided, and time began to make sense again. They constantly monitored my blood pressure and pulse daily and drew blood every other day. It was important for them to know all my vitals and to monitor my medications.

The hospital itself was considerably different than French Hospital. It was more relaxed and housed less severe patients. There were also more freedoms, frequent interactions with other patients, and a greater selection of activities. And gorgeous views! There was a fair amount of supervision, but the focus was more on medication dispensing.

Many of the patients suffered with addiction, PTSD, and depression. One of the patients became addicted to pain medication from a severe back injury. He needed another back surgery, but his doctor wouldn't perform the surgery until he was clean from the pain medication. Another young woman was court-ordered to deal with alcohol addiction. These scenarios were endless and were only shared by the patient themselves. I was basically the "odd man out," as I was the only manic on the unit.

A camaraderie among the patients gradually developed. We knew who liked salsa or butter, and we would order extra to share. When someone was having a tough day, we would bus their dinner trays. Sometimes we would just sit with someone. It was touching, to say the least.

Our activities on the ward included Alcoholics Anonymous, Narcotics Anonymous, yoga, problem-solving, art exploration, and more. The classes were nonthreatening, and I attended most of them. Of course, I journaled feverishly. Some of my entries were crystal clear while other entries were quite fuzzy.

We were allowed visitors for one hour per day. Since we lived so far away (one and a half hours), the family set up a schedule. Amanda decorated my room, and my sister brought me clothes. The hospital tightly controlled the flow of visitors, keeping the chaos to a minimum.

It was a treat to see someone familiar, although it was often tiring. I sometimes felt judged, maybe analyzed, by those who loved me the most. They were assessing my improvement. One of my daughters,

Heidi, read part of my journal and was concerned that my depression might be causing me to focus on the negative. We took turns writing in the journal, and I saw some progress. She challenged me to log "grateful" words, and I discovered many: *crisp mornings, electricity, fruit trees, music, clean sheets, kids giggling, my husband's strength, playing cards with my granddaughter, Sugar (my puppy), veterans, parental love, barn kitties, and cut grass.* The list went on and on.

A problem arose with my cell phone. In my full-on manic state, I began to call random people—my nephew, our business partners. I overshared some things that were on my mind, things that shouldn't have been mentioned. Some of the people had no idea about my medical condition and expressed a concern to Karl concerning my well-being. He quickly made a change in the cell phone usage. My personal phone was confiscated, and he gave me a temporary phone with only certain numbers downloaded. This stopped me in my tracks! I didn't much like his control, but I lived with it.

Other than the day-to-day treatment, our group of patients experienced a glorious July Fourth holiday. The staff gained clearance for us to enjoy the fireworks show happening off the coast of Santa Barbara. Granted, we weren't bussed or released, but we were escorted from floor to floor via elevators and corridors to secure the best vantage point. It was planned at the very last minute. Having been relegated to the indoors for several days, the "freedom" and the fresh air were exhilarating. Never have fireworks been so bright, so clear! We had all been fighting our individual demons for so long that these moments allowed us immeasurable joy and camaraderie. This event, along with the popcorn, gave us the energy to move forward.

Medication management was probably the most important function of the hospital. The dispensary was available several times a day, but it was the patient's responsibility to keep track of his medication schedule. For me, it was exhausting since my medications often changed dramatically. Sometimes the change was in the dosage; other times it was an entirely different drug. There was an accountability on our part; we were to know our meds.

This is perhaps the reason I stayed in the hospital for several days. It takes time to assess the reactions of the drugs. Some medications take weeks or even months to reach the maximum effectiveness, and the combinations of drugs pose side effects. We all absorb the medications differently, and the doctor may need to adjust. It can be a matter of trial and error.

One of the medications that I began taking again was Zyprexa, a psychiatric medication originally developed for the treatment of schizophrenia and bipolar illness. It has now gained widespread use for the treatment of depression. For me, it was used to sedate my manic mood, to slow me down. Over a two-month period of time, I gained thirty pounds. This side effect was not explained to me. If I had known, I would have declined the prescription. Later, I did some research. It takes roughly two years to purge this drug from your system. Thirty pounds is a lot of weight, and it was a real struggle to lose it.

Having stabilized after eight days, I was released. The hospital encouraged rest and supervision. With these parameters, we felt that a patient in-care treatment facility might be an option. Most beds were filled in Southern California, and most would not take insurance—cash only. We located a facility that would accept me for two weeks at a price tag of $15,000. We drove to the facility, and I was aghast at the condition of the house—dark, no street signs or yard, crumbs on the counter, disorganized intake procedure, and young women milling about aimlessly. After a quick tour, I told Karl that I couldn't stay there and we should find somewhere else. We left and promptly stopped payment on the check. Here we witnessed another huge rip-off in terms of mental health care.

In lieu of this residential treatment facility, we headed to a hotel on the Pacific Coast, where I could have some peace and quiet for about a week—nowhere near $15,000. This choice was actually a good one. I've been told that when the brain experiences this kind of trauma, a type of temporary damage occurs. The hotel had room service, a hot tub, and a spa. What more did I need?

I really don't think that my stay at Cottage Hospital was as traumatic as my time at French Hospital. Perhaps we discovered the problem earlier. Perhaps it was because we had been through this before. Perhaps my mania was less severe and easier to "reel in." Perhaps the doctors had more medication choices. Dr. Bauman handled the entire process with professionalism and empathy. She was in my corner at every turn.

Whatever the reason, I made it through the darkness somewhat unscathed. My fear is that the dragon can raise its ugly head at any point it chooses; therefore, I need to be vigilant with my prevention maintenance and stay in close contact with my physician.

16

THE NET WIDENS

When my "vacation" in Santa Barbara ended, we sought a new approach to my mental illness, my bipolar condition. Our "family team" was always open to avoiding another train wreck, and we looked outside my box to change the method of treatment. There was a trend to use both the services of a psychiatrist *and* a psychologist—one for medication management and one for day-to-day, week-to-week, month-to-month talk therapy. This would prove both economically sound and allow for greater accessibility to mental health services. With my regular psychiatrist practicing in San Luis Obispo, we looked for a local psychologist, and I received a glowing referral from my best friend.

Enter a new face, a breath of fresh air, a listener, and she came in with four-inch stiletto heels—Dr. Tia Glickman, LMFT, PhD! She developed a heads-up approach to my treatment. My family has an open line to her phone in regard to my mental health, and she helps to keep any symptoms at bay. This shortens the lag time for deciding on a course of action. If, in fact, she determines that Dr. Bauman needs a call, that is my cue to take the next step. Two of my children have already utilized this plan, and it has worked like clockwork; no need to make the second call.

Psychiatry today primarily focuses on diagnosis and medication rather than education, relationships, or social functioning. A psychologist or therapist provides the "talk therapy"—the "tools," per se, for growth and understanding. The opportunity to heal injured parts from the past takes time and insight, and this is often what the psychiatrist has little time to explore. I am always open to both discussion and exploration.

For me, it is important to have as many connections regarding my mental health as possible. The more professionals that know me and are able to help with my struggles, the more likely that my episodes will be thwarted and I will remain healthy. Catching my signs early on is a must. As a family, we are the first line of defense; next come the professionals. It may seem a bit dramatic, but my life is often in their hands.

Dr. Glickman and I had a few meetings, and then she began to talk to my children, my sister, and my husband in order to gain information about me and my illness. She felt that she was able to open the door to my bipolar illness, but was amazed at their lack of understanding. The family had received very little education and was tragically ignorant of my illness as a whole.

Early on, Dr. Glickman felt that a family meeting might trigger some much-needed interaction. All were in attendance except my children's spouses. I was apprehensive, afraid of what they might express and of what my reactions might be. I remember sitting in front, next to the doctor, reminding myself that all I had to do was listen. But the listening proved to be horrendous. My family spewed years and years of pent-up frustration. I had been warned this was likely to happen and that they needed to vent. They viewed me as unwilling to participate in family activities. For me, it had been easier to say no to activities than it was to say yes. I had never heard that they had missed me before. I had always thought that the invitations were made out of common courtesy. Many of their concerns were from incidents years ago, some of which I could hardly remember.

To some degree, my family relationships have improved. I am consciously saying yes more frequently and allowing myself to live in the moment. The grandkids like to visit, and I like to tell them yes. There is really no reason to say no. If you say no too many times, they will just stop asking.

So my talk therapy continues. Sometimes our discussions are profound, and other times they are uneventful. But even if they are not substantive, the talks continue to provide my therapist with information about me. An accurate assessment, combined with the necessary tools, is all that I really need.

17

QUESTIONS AND MORE QUESTIONS

Hopefully, we are surrounded by family and friends during our life's struggles. I had that luxury. There was, however, a real gap in communication on many levels. This shielding of both the children and me prevented a lot of understanding and potential healing among all of us. Some of the forthcoming thoughts and observations were telling and even raw to me. How could the situations have occurred? Why did I not see the consequences of my actions?

Some of these incidents were very intense for my friends and family. This disease affects all of us, and *their* voices need to be heard. Some expressed their hesitancy to answer questions. They did not want to bring added hurt to me and did not want to rehash the subject. But it's time to unload. I gathered some pertinent questions and recorded my loved ones' responses.

NANCI, My Sister

When did you discover that I was ill?

It was during the fair, July 1979. Chad was just born. Mom and I talked about your incessant talking. I was mad at myself because I didn't have the skills to help stop the manic progression.

What did you think of my hospitalization at French Hospital?

I remember visiting frequently, maybe every other day. The hospital would search my purse for pens, combs, anything which could be made into something sharp. It would then be confiscated. At this point I want to say something about generational family secrets. It was decided that we wouldn't tell anyone outside of our little circle. This thought process continued throughout your illness. In some ways it did you harm, knowing the illness was something for which to be ashamed.

What were some of my most notable episodes of mania?

You were always talking, sharing random thoughts. Your mind didn't settle down. On a trip to Vegas, you bought a pair of $700 handmade leather shoes. My daughter couldn't believe that you had spent that kind of money. You also went to the coast, sat on a bench, and gave money to the homeless.

What were some of my most notable episodes of depression?

I have not noticed much depression.

What do you foresee in my future?

I see good things. You are in a good space. I must address your stay at Santa Barbara Cottage Hospital. I felt you were much more in control there. You attended classes and made friends. I felt that you got hard-core help and returned healed—125 percent.

SHARON, My Friend of Forty Years

When did you discover I was ill?

Many years ago. You were very good at disguising it and always putting on a happy exterior. Looking back, it was obvious on our train trip to Reno that something was amiss. It turned out to be your reaction to your breast cancer diagnosis. You kept the reason a secret at the time (an obvious reaction), but the fact that you wanted to be alone and sleep was probably a bit of depression creeping in to add to a scary time in your life.

What did you think about my hospitalization at French?

I think you are talking about your stay after your group trip to Europe when so many on the trip had been ill. Our sister, Judy, had been very ill on the trip, so I kept asking her how you were doing. Again, everything was kept secret, and I was led to believe you were sicker than the rest of the people on your trip. I was very scared for you, but didn't learn about the real reason you were hospitalized until much later. When I did find out, I was proud of you for seeking help. I was glad you were accepting the help. I have seen firsthand what happens to a person and her family when they refuse to recognize there is a problem and won't accept any help.

Were you ever frightened for me?

Yes. You are a dear friend, and this illness takes on so many different faces and moods that it makes it hard to manage an even keel. All of your friends were so proud of you for talking to us at a sorority meeting several years ago. I felt this was such a breakthrough because it kind of gave us permission to ask you questions about your illness so we could better understand what you were going through and find out how, or if, we could help. I know talking to you has helped me understand not only what you were experiencing but also what my sister has been going through with her similar illness. Thank you for opening up to us.

What were some of my most notable manic episodes?

I haven't experienced any notable episodes. Most people in our group of friends tend to be strong and outspoken at times, so it's hard to tell. My own family can document three generations of bipolar illness. It is very scary at times when everything goes completely off the rails, and it's so hard to regain any control.

What were some of my most notable episodes of depression?

Again, I haven't experienced an actual episode.

What do you foresee in my future?

I think your book will open a whole new chapter in your life. You will open a line of communication for so many others, and I believe that by doing this you will be able to better navigate your own ups and downs. I'm not sure if there will ever be a cure for everything, but this dialogue is bound to help you while helping others in the process. You took the first step long ago by actually realizing the illness was there and by seeking answers.

KARL, My Husband

When did you discover I was ill?

When you started staying up day and night and repeating yourself over and over. You were crying a lot and were very emotional, probably June and July of 1979.

What did you think of my hospitalization at French Hospital?

We kind of knew what to expect. We were glad that we found Dr. Speed. I was always busy with the kids, but always thought you would get better.

Were you ever frightened?

Before you were first admitted to General Hospital, I was afraid that you would continue on your downward spiral.

What were some of my most notable episodes of depression?

This does not apply since Cindy had very little depression.

What do you foresee in my future?

With vigilant attention to correct medication and proper rest, we should be good to make it another forty-eight years (our anniversary). I think we can ride it on out.

MARY, My Friend of Sixty Years

When did you discover I was ill?

The first time I knew that there was something wrong was not too long after the birth of Chad. I tried to visit you and became concerned when your family kept me away. I was eventually told that you were in the hospital with postpartum depression, and your mom let me come and see you and Chad. I was very grateful. You were not allowed to be left alone with Chad. You gradually got better, and things seemed to return to normal.

What did you think of my hospitalization at French?

I did not know a lot about your hospitalization at French Hospital. Again, your mom told me that you were in the mental health facility of French Hospital as you needed some rest. I still did not know what your diagnosis was.

Were you ever frightened for me?

The first time that you had to be put in the hospital when Chad was so little, it scared the shit out of me. They kept saying it was postpartum depression, and that's what I believed for years and years until you were admitted to French. When the girls were born, I was so afraid it was going to happen again. But I knew we were all watching for it and kept a good eye on you; everything seemed to go pretty well.

What were some of my most notable episodes of mania?

I have always looked at you as being a little bit manic. But I have chalked it up to—it's just your personality. Everything in your house has to be in its proper place and cleaned to a T. It's never bothered me; in fact, I always admired your energy. It took a lot to accomplish all the things that you could do in one day. I am still amazed at that. I have also wished that I could be like you and have everything in my life in order. At least it appears to everyone that your life is in order when I, in fact, know that it's not.

What were some of my most notable episodes of depression?

I have never seen you in a depressive episode.

What do you foresee in my future?

I see what I have always seen. A beautiful person inside and out, with people who love her more than I could ever explain. You are a survivor, and I am very proud to call you my friend, or rather, my best friend. You have set a wonderful example of how a person should live their life in love, in giving and in caring. I see your future as being nothing but successful.

CHAD, My Son

When did you discover I was ill?

In 1998, when you entered French Hospital. I knew something was wrong, but didn't know what it was. At about four years old, I would see you cry. You would say things like, "Just throw me away." Dad always said that he would take care of things.

What did you think of my hospitalization at French Hospital?

It was sad, terrible, almost like a prison.

Were you ever frightened?

Never.

What were some of my most notable episodes of mania?

You cleaned and vacuumed in the middle of the night. When you started to work on your book, you showed signs of mania. This time when you started to work on your book, the mania didn't start. I believe hormones and menopause contributed somehow to the mania.

What were some of my most notable episodes of depression?

It seemed like depression when you were drugged in the hospital. Then, when you slept 8 a.m. to 8 p.m., it was more evident.

Could you notice my depression? When did it become apparent?

It became apparent after you came out of the hospital. But mostly, you never really seemed depressed; it was always the mania.

What do you foresee in my future?

I think you will be balanced and lead a healthy life. Continue on the path you are on.

Are you concerned that you might have bipolar tendencies?

I am concerned that I might have Mom's illness. I deal with anxiety and have had significant bouts of depression. Now when I'm happy, I'm much happier. I have swings that are wider than a normal person's. The swings have lessened since I quit drinking. This choice has allowed me to evaluate what is best for me.

HEIDI, My Daughter

When did you discover I was ill?

I began seeing a change when you were diagnosed with cancer and the house was being remodeled. Around 1999.

What did you think of my hospitalization at French Hospital?

No one ever said why you were there. You just left, and we didn't know why. At the time I never knew what was actually happening. All everyone would say was that you were sick. Honestly, I just tried to protect myself and stay away and not make anyone upset.

Were you ever frightened?

When you came home, you were a different person. I didn't know you. I was always afraid.

What were some of my most notable episodes of mania?

Memory loss, rage, spending money. You didn't make sense a lot of the time.

What were some of my notable episodes of depression?

You said that you wanted to die.

Could you notice my depression? When did it become apparent?

You quit going to the gym, cooking dinner. You also slept all the time.

What do you foresee in my future?

I hope you can get to a place where you don't sweat the small stuff; love the kids despite their messes and imperfections. Try to go back to the gym, eat healthy, and get in shape. Enjoy life and home! I want you to be happy *whatever* that looks like.

Are you concerned for yourself that this bipolar illness might be hereditary?

Yes, I am concerned. One in three children is diagnosed with bipolar illness if he has a parent with the disease. I worry about our life expectancy and dementia.

AMANDA, My Daughter

When did you discover I was ill?

I was in the eighth grade at the family lake reunion. Nana said you were sick, and Popo kept crying. She didn't tell the whole truth.

What did you think of my hospitalization at French Hospital?

Chad came home crying and said that you were in a hospital that was like a jail. Then I knew something was really wrong. Again, no one said anything else.

Were you ever frightened?

Not frightened, just confused. Why was my mom sleeping all the time? Why could she not take care of anyone else? Why did I have to watch over her?

What were some of my most notable episodes of mania?

You tried to purchase the Methodist church in Shandon while hospitalized in Cottage Hospital, Santa Barbara. I thought if you started to spend all your money that we would need to have power of attorney over your estate.

What were some of my most notable episodes of depression?

You were sleeping for what seemed like months. You experienced constant sadness.

Could you notice my depression? When did it become apparent?

I didn't really know it was depression. I just thought it was you. You were tired, sad, unmotivated, and pessimistic.

What do you foresee in my future?

I'm proud of you and your efforts to get well. You are seeing a counselor, exercising, making time for the grandkids, and have the ability to care for others. I pray it continues.

Are you concerned for yourself that this bipolar illness might be hereditary?

Sometimes I am.

CONCLUSION

As you can see, the answers to my questions are varied and thoughtful. What I can see is that I have a network of people who have surrounded me with love throughout this crazy, confusing journey. I have had strong allies in both my family members and my friends. Even in the toughest of times, I have never been alone.

18

SOMEONE LIKE ME

This chapter is the result of a required assignment. In order to secure an agent for book publishing, there is a mountain of information that an author must compile. This submission is in conjunction with the actual manuscript. One of the submissions is that of "Competing Books," a thoughtful comparison of roughly five books on similar subjects. So in order to comply with the submission assignment, I needed to *read* these "appropriate" books and then compare them with *When the Brakes Fail*. This feat would not be as easy as I initially thought.

The very first book I chose to reread was *An Unquiet Mind* by Kay Redfield Jamison. At the time of its publication, it was a must-read for anyone interested in manic depression. The author was a psychiatrist, so her story was particularly unique. Dr. Nancy Speed, my psychiatrist at the time, highly recommended the book, and I quickly bought an additional eight copies for my family and friends (sound a tad manic, eh?). I still have four copies—apparently not many takers. The book highlights many of the ideas that I have put forth in *When the Brakes Fail*: noncompliance with medication management, silence and confusion about the illness in the workplace, the lack of enjoyment while in a depressive state, and overspending while manic. Just the title of the book, *An Unquiet Mind*, conjures up my state of mind when I couldn't stop it from racing.

Even with the illness, Ms. Jamison excelled in her career. Surprisingly, the medical community embraced her even with the revelation of the illness. I, too, have had success in my career; but unlike Ms. Jamison, I did not share my illness with my employer for fear of reprisal. In the end, I became my own employer and set my own schedule, keeping my illness in mind. This allowed me to self-manage while finding meaningful success in my career.

Another interesting read was *Madness* by Marya Hornbacher. Her mania was exhausting, detailed in rapid-fire mood swings. The book was long, with condensed spacing and little relief, without chapter breaks. I did understand the author's "mind chatter," but it could be confusing to the average reader. Perhaps this bombardment of details was meant to demonstrate the mania itself. My mania might seem this intense to my family, but it never seems that intense to me. With mania, everyone else can see the monumental chaos—everyone but the person spinning out of control. The book repeats itself, but that is also the pattern of the mania. The book had a great bibliography, and it is no wonder that it is a *New York Times* bestseller.

And . . . as the mania cycles out, then comes the depression. In *A Memoir of Love and Madness*, the author, Rahla Xenopousos, explains, "Some days a familiar sadness encroaches on my enchanted universe, a parasite insidiously eating away at my life. Happiness leaks out of my being. Then I take to bed, go into hiding."

This hiding is common, the easy way out, the escape from any interaction with the world, including my family. Every excuse is devised to eliminate communication: headache, sore back, lack of sleep. I ask myself, what right do I have to be a wife and a mother? Wouldn't it be better if I were gone? Suicide, anorexia, and self-mutilation were never an option for me, so I found the least intrusive way to exist.

In *Stairway to Madness*, author Angelica says, "Living with bipolar illness has not been easy. You have to constantly be on alert as to how you are feeling inside, which is something only you can truly know. In this sense, you can feel very alone." Alone in madness and alone in grief. There are consequences to my every thought. With depression, there is too little effort put into life. With mania, there is too much effort. Such a balancing act to find the middle ground!

Toward the end of yet another book, *Yellow Tulips*, the author, Helen Joy George, states, "It doesn't end, friends. I wrote this book with mania running through my veins. I wrote it slumped in a chair. I wrote it sobbing, naked on the floor. I scratched it onto bits of paper and I spoke it into my phone. I want to control my story." Her thoughts explain my need to write this book. Whatever it takes to share my life, my complicated life, with you, my readers. This urgency is the momentum of my thoughts. Though we are all different, we are also the same.

I experienced a tidal wave of emotions as I read each book. The bravery of the authors was undeniable. The stories were so close to my story that I was often lost in the details. At times I had to physically separate myself from the books so that I didn't disappear into the pages. The success of a good book is to motivate the reader to feel the words. Most of the books did just that—I was almost swallowed whole by their words. I had to channel my thoughts to thwart the entry of the madness. When I am well, it is easy to do.

There exists a similar thread, which is woven through those suffering with bipolar illness. Interestingly, through these books . . . I found someone like me.

19

ON MY SOAPBOX

A soapbox is a platform or crate that is used as a makeshift stand by a public speaker. It actually provides the speaker an opportunity to air her views publicly without reprisal. With this book, I suppose I have become a public speaker. Here I speak my truths and concerns:

- There is a *basic lack of understanding* in regard to mental illness. An illness is an illness, whether it be diabetes or clinical depression. It certainly is not a character flaw. Nearly *one* in five adults in the United States lives with a mental illness, which makes it a huge problem. Each illness has its own characteristics, and each diagnosis is made specifically for each individual.

- There exists *a stigma in society* regarding mental illness. This stigma often causes the person to wrestle with very real dilemmas and make choices. The stigma, which accompanies the illness, can cause a person to refuse help and to suffer in silence. The American Psychiatric Association says, "More than half of the people with mental illness don't receive help for their disorders. Often people avoid or delay seeking treatment due to concerns about being treated differently, or fears of losing their jobs and livelihood. That's because stigma, prejudice and discrimination against people with mental illness is still very much a problem." The notion that everyone has a perfectly balanced life is nonsense. Mental illness not only causes great pain to its sufferers but can remove them from society. It can cause them to become unproductive or counterproductive. Society as a whole suffers because they suffer. Society is only as good as its individual parts.

- Patients with severe mental illness often have *little or no access* to adequate medication, psychological counseling, social support, or housing. Again, this lack of access alienates and perpetuates the divisiveness of the disease.

- There is a *shortage of psychiatrists* in the United States. According to a 2018 report by Merritt Hawkins, a physician search firm, there are about nine psychiatrists per one hundred thousand Americans. In order to provide true quality care, that ratio should be fifteen psychiatrists per one hundred thousand Americans. In our small county, the number of psychiatrists is surprisingly low. Most of the psychiatrists in our area do not accept new patients, leaving the mentally ill on the outside looking in.

- *General practitioners* are dispensing psychotropic drugs without much training, and there is a problem of massive over-treatment. I know about this firsthand. People in general are reaching out to any physician for help, but they are often not getting the proper diagnoses and treatment. Rushed primary care doctors are anxious to dispense medication quickly. When I got the courage to disclose my illness to my general practitioner, he made no attempt to emotionally connect with me, only leaving me with more shame. The stigma raised its ugly head once again. Simply ordering a prescription does not solve the problem. A psychiatric assessment needs to occur prior to the dispensing of medication.

- *Health insurance* is a major component when it comes to mental health. Basically, it is nonexistent. Insurance coverage is generally only available for a "seen" malady, not an "unseen" malady. The brain is the most important organ in the body, but it is the organ that is most ignored and the least likely to be treated. I had good medical insurance, and two of my three hospital stays were not covered.

- I am currently a "cash pay" patient with both my psychiatrist and psychologist. The insurance companies do not reimburse the doctors fairly, *especially* in rural areas, so they, in turn, must operate their businesses as cash only. So once again, it becomes a struggle between the "haves" and the "have-nots." If you have enough money, you can get the services. If you don't have the funds, you are out of luck. This logic is grossly unfair to any medical treatment. These are very real concerns and are frankly embarrassing for the most developed country in the world.

- If the insurance companies would *promote preventative medicine* rather than just putting out fires, our society would be healthier. Patients would improve, and it would actually be savings—a win-win. Virtual medicine, hopefully, will continue to make strides in health care.

- There is a large mental health component with *homelessness*. It is difficult to dispense medications to a migrant population, let alone coordinate therapy services. The illnesses will continue to spiral out of control if not kept in check. If medication and treatment are not available, sufferers turn to other measures to manage their demons: alcohol, marijuana, and illicit street drugs. Services need to be rendered at the local level, to reach the patients in their backyards. If we don't go to them, the mental illness conundrum will continue to hemorrhage.

- *Additional problems* of suicide, employment issues, family conflict, and physical health problems can all be linked to mental health concerns. The list of problems is endless.

- The number of *short-term inpatient psychiatric beds* is staggeringly low. We do not have a unit in our county, and so I was forced to travel for treatment. Family support systems suffer because of this distance. In-patient facilities provide physicians a better avenue of treatment for the patient. The psychotropic drugs take a while to work for each patient, and there is a trial-and-error component to it all. When a person can stay in a facility for a longer period of time, the result can be much more measurable. Once again, it all comes down to money.

Mental health is not a quick fix. Most of the time, both talk therapy and medication are needed. If you don't have access to all the tools, your time might be wasted. There needs to be a collective realization that a major problem exists.

Our government needs to play an active part in the solution: it is the main controller of the funding! The solution needs to be a collaborative effort. The best of the best is required to find the right solutions. I've read countless plans regarding mental illness. Funding is procured for all sorts of other projects, but mental illness is usually overlooked. How many politicians are sufficiently informed to make competent decisions about mental health?

My "unofficial public speaking" is through this book. I have stepped on my soapbox to tell you about the most important social issue of my life. There are many others who share this same story. It is really our duty to tell our stories and inform the masses. Each one of you has the opportunity to tell someone *your* story—your neighbor, your congressman, your family. Your revelation might make a difference. Someone knows someone, who knows someone . . .

Drag out the soapboxes so that the world will be forced to listen. It's our charge to take care of one another, especially those who cannot petition for themselves.

20
AND FINALLY . . .

How did a college-educated honor student, mother of three, wife of forty-eight years, grandmother to seven, teacher, chief financial officer, and author "run off the rails"? It seems unlikely, but here I am—functioning at a high level with a few minor glitches. Mental illness does not discriminate: it takes whom it wishes, whenever it wants.

Amid the facts and figures that I have presented to you, my own truth is really the only truth that I know. It is both all at once immeasurable and indescribable. To finally grasp and accept the fact that I cannot be all things to all people has been freeing. A song by the Brothers Osborne, "I'm Not for Everyone," in part tells my story:

I'm always speaking my mind
When I'm better off biting my tongue
I'm a bad joke at the wrong time
Hell, I'm a legend in my own mind
I'm good for some, but I'm not for everyone.

Frankly, it's okay for me to be different. That resolution has been a long time coming. There have been times when I wasn't available for my family. Our family was operating in virgin territory, and we—or I—

made tons of mistakes. It would have been easier to have done it alone, but I didn't have that option.

For the most part, communication in our family has been lacking. Tough issues were buried. It has always been our best course of action. Serious issues were not tackled head-on. There are some issues that we can't discuss, even years later. There is no means of resolution if ideas cannot be discussed. Many issues were resolved without my input.

I will forever be questioned regarding my decisions. Family members ask, "Is it the bipolar illness speaking, or is it Mom?" I feel that they are quick to judge, with little room for forgiveness. To this day, some of the family hurts have never been released. I long to understand the hurts, but as I've mentioned, there really isn't an opportunity for meaningful discussion.

Other than a lack of family communication, my biggest dilemma has been the shroud of shame. At times, the shame attached to the illness was almost too much to bear. There was an associated flaw, a deficit of sorts, that only I could comprehend. My self-confidence was diminished, and there was a hole in my soul, never to be shared with others.

In this "not telling" comes the notion of secrecy. Confession is risky. Who could I trust? The notion of rejection was paramount, especially if people knew my whole truth. So I sat on my story, revealing very little to anyone.

My talks with my therapists have been immensely helpful. They provide me insights into my choices and allow me to explore without retribution. Our discussions have enabled me to seek my ever-changing truth. They are neutral facilitators, not necessarily problem-solvers.

They have seen many bipolar sufferers like me and know both the joys and the pitfalls.

Over the years, whenever I talked about writing this book, my family would surmise that I was beginning to spin off into a manic state or that I was just being a "wacko mom." I would receive the "rolling-eye look." Granted, I have talked about this book for years, but I do have something to say, something that might be consequential to someone. *That* someone could be you. You have now become my confidant, someone I can trust with my secret.

My secrets are often in question form. My most haunting question is: *Will this madness happen again, and when?* This fear is so real that I can barely say the words. On the one hand, I want the doctor to tell me, "Never," but on the other hand, I know there are no guarantees. The mania becomes a raging dragon, swallowing my soul and spitting me out when it chooses. I have no say in the matter.

I have done all the right things—medication management, therapy, and self-care—and in the long run, those things favorably contribute to my general health. However, there are no promises. The doctor reassures me that we have a definitive plan in place and that she is confident that a full-blown episode could be easily averted. And that notion of trust surfaces again. She is my lifeline to my future.

My circle of friends continues to widen, and with this comes additional trust. In the last month I shared my mental health issues with a women's group in a casual setting. There were several ladies who did not know about my illness, some of whom I had known for years. We openly discussed their stories and the stories of their loved ones. We shared in a very healthy way, and they were so supportive, listening to my story with great empathy. We spoke about society and its reaction to mental illness. Every conversation provides an opportunity for education. They showed a real interest in my upcoming book. This genuine encouragement is uplifting.

I have also been encouraged by a small group of Christian women. We meet for lunch weekly. As I composed chapters for this book, I brought them to the group. As a group, they would either approve or disapprove, always making mindful comments. There was even a chapter that they vetoed, deciding it could be construed as too hurtful. Their judgment won out, and the chapter was scrapped. My journey surely includes these ladies.

It's odd to think that this will be my final chapter to you. I have longed to tie my words together so that you might understand my life. I pieced together my story and, through me, I hope that you have the courage to tell your story, whatever that might be. Figure out what you want to say about your illness, and blurt it out. Find a friend. Tell your doctor. Read a book. Query a topic on the internet. Establish a dialogue with others. There is a plethora of avenues to guide you. Your story could be someone else's story, and someone else's story could be yours. You now know my story; hopefully, it will make a difference to you.

Choosing a title for this book was challenging, but I kept revisiting the comment that my initial general practitioner explained—the illness is like a roaring, out-of-control freight train. But . . . eventually, the train will stop, and your opportunities will present themselves. Pick up the pieces; sift through the mess you did not anticipate. The wreck may seem disastrous, or even unsurmountable, but there is always light at the end of the tunnel. Follow the light.

ACKNOWLEDGMENTS

First and foremost, I give thanks to my competent doctors and psychologists: Dr. George Johnson, Dr. Nancy Speed, Dr. Margaret Bauman, and Dr. Tia Glickman. Living in a rural area, it was remarkable that I found such progressive medical professionals.

•

My best friend of over sixty years, Mary, has loved me through it all—no judgments, no shame. She's a once-in-a-lifetime ally.

•

My parents and my sister have rallied around me time and time again. There was never a moment that I felt alone. They held me close, even when they didn't fully understand.

•

This book is a stark reminder of our family's struggles. I applaud my children for attempting to understand my mental health toils.

•

My Thursday lunch group of seven kept me grounded and regularly edited my chapters. I encouraged them to provide me with honest, much-needed advice. Bernie was my loudest cheerleader and would have loved to see this finished project.

•

My two local editors, Sean and Malei Weir, were both insightful and gentle with their manuscript changes.

•

I have belonged to a women's group for perhaps forty years. Two years ago I explained my illness to them. They listened and continued to support me.

•

Probably the most important supporter in my journey is my husband, Karl. He has been patient and has encouraged me to find treatment. He continues to be my rock.

CINDY CARMINATI WITTSTROM

Cindy has been on a fast train most of her life. She has experienced a myriad of things, including a strong family unit, supportive friends, church, and extensive travel.

Her heart, however, is strongly connected to marginalized communities. As an advocate she has made, and continues to make, a tremendous difference for those in need.

Over the years she has participated in many organizations, working directly with children and clients. She has championed the causes of: Loaves and Fishes (a local food bank); CASA (Court Appointed Special Advocates for abused and neglected children);

American Cancer Society; Juvenile Justice and Delinquency Prevention Commission; ECHO (homeless shelter and services); and many after-school programs.

Cindy's illnesses have, in a way, been positive because they have allowed her to speak for others. She has both an insight and a heart to accomplish many changes in this confusing, runaway world.

Cindy's Website:

CindyWittstrom.com